# STUDENT UNIT GUIDE

## NEW EDITION

## Edexcel AS Chemistry Unit 1
## The Core Principles of Chemistry

Rod Beavon and George Facer

PHILIP ALLAN

Philip Allan Updates, an imprint of Hodder Education, an Hachette UK company, Market Place, Deddington, Oxfordshire OX15 0SE

*Orders*
Bookpoint Ltd, 130 Milton Park, Abingdon, Oxfordshire, OX14 4SB
tel: 01235 827827
fax: 01235 400401
e-mail: uk.orders@bookpoint.co.uk
Lines are open 9.00 a.m.–5.00 p.m., Monday to Saturday, with a 24-hour message answering service.
You can also order through the Philip Allan Updates website: www.philipallan.co.uk

ISBN 978-1-4441-6260-8

First printed 2012
Impression number 5 4 3 2 1
Year 2017 2016 2015 2014 2013 2012

Cover photo: Fotolia

Printed in Dubai

Hachette UK's policy is to use papers that are natural, renewable and recyclable products and made from wood grown in sustainable forests. The logging and manufacturing processes are expected to conform to the environmental regulations of the country of origin.

P02006

# Contents

# Getting the most from this book

**Examiner tips**
Advice from the examiner on key points in the text to help you learn and recall unit content, avoid pitfalls, and polish your exam technique in order to boost your grade.

**Knowledge check**
Rapid-fire questions throughout the Content Guidance section to check your understanding.

**Knowledge check answers**
**1** Turn to the back of the book for the Knowledge check answers.

**Summary**

**Summaries**
- Each core topic is rounded off by a bullet-list summary for quick-check reference of what you need to know.

## Questions & Answers

**Exam-style questions**

**Examiner comments on the questions**
Tips on what you need to do to gain full marks, indicated by the icon **e**.

**Sample student answers**
Practise the questions, then look at the student answers that follow each set of questions.

**Examiner commentary on sample student answers**
Find out how many marks each answer would be awarded in the exam and then read the examiner comments (preceded by the icon **e**) following each student answer. Annotations that link back to points made in the student answers show exactly how and where marks are gained or lost.

# About this book

This unit guide is the first of a series covering the Edexcel specification for AS and A2 chemistry. It offers advice for the effective study of **Unit 1: The Core Principles of Chemistry**. Its aim is to help you understand the chemistry — it is not intended as a shopping list, enabling you to cram for an examination. The guide has two sections:

- **Content Guidance** — this section is not intended to be a textbook. It offers guidelines on the main features of the content of Unit 1, together with particular advice on making study more productive.
- **Questions & Answers** — this section starts with an introduction that gives advice on approaches and techniques, to ensure you answer the examination questions in the best way that you can. It then provides Unit 1-style questions, with student answers and examiner comments.

The effective understanding of chemistry requires time. No one suggests it is an easy subject, but even those who find it difficult can overcome their problems by the proper investment of time.

To understand the chemistry, you have to make links between the various topics. The subject is coherent; it is not a collection of discrete modules. These links only come with experience, which means time spent thinking about chemistry, working with it and solving chemical problems. Time produces fluency with the ideas. If you have that, together with good technique, the examination will look after itself. Don't be an examination automaton — be a chemist.

## The specification

The specification states the chemistry that can be used in the unit tests and describes the format of those tests. It can be obtained from Edexcel, either as a printed document or from the web at **www.edexcel.org.uk**.

## Learning to learn

Learning is not instinctive — you have to develop suitable techniques to make your use of time effective. In particular, chemistry has peculiar difficulties that need to be understood if your studies are to be effective from the start.

### Planning

Busy people do not achieve what they do by approaching life haphazardly. They plan — so that if they are working they mean to be working, and if they are watching television they have planned to do so. Planning is essential. You *must* know what you have to do each day and set aside time to do it. Furthermore, to devote time to study means you may have to give something up that you are already doing. There is no way that you can generate extra hours in the day.

Be realistic in your planning. You cannot work all the time, and you must build in time for recreation and family responsibilities.

## Targets

When devising your plan, have a target for each study period. This might be a particular section of the specification, or it might be rearranging information from text into pictures, or drawing a flowchart relating all the reactions of group 1 and group 2. Whatever it is, be determined to master your target material before you leave it.

## Reading chemistry textbooks

A page of chemistry may have a range of material that differs widely in difficulty. Therefore, the speed at which the various parts of a page can be read may have to vary, if it is to be understood. In addition, you should read with pencil and paper to hand and jot things down as you go, for example, equations, diagrams and questions to be followed up. If you do not write the questions down, you will forget them; if you do not master detail, you will never become fluent in chemistry.

### Text

This is the easiest part to read, and little advice is needed here.

### Chemical equations

Equations are used because they are quantitative, concise and internationally understood. Take time over them, copy them and check that they balance. Most of all, try to visualise what is happening as the reaction proceeds. If you can't, make a note to ask someone who can or — even better — ask your teacher to *show* you the reaction if at all possible. Chemical equations describe real processes; they are not abstract algebraic constructs.

### Graphs

Graphs give a lot of information, and they must be understood in detail rather than as a general impression. Take time over them. Note what the axes are, what the units are, the shape of the graph and what the shape means in chemical terms.

### Tables

Tables are a means of displaying a lot of information. You need to be aware of the table headings and the units of numerical entries. Take time over them. What trends can be seen? How do these relate to chemical properties? Sometimes it can be useful to convert tables of data into graphs.

### Diagrams

Diagrams of apparatus should be drawn in section. When you see them, copy them and ask yourself why the apparatus has the features that it has. What is the difference between a distillation and a reflux apparatus, for example? When you do practical work, examine each piece of the apparatus closely so that you know both its form and function.

## Calculations

Do not take calculations on trust — work through them. First, make certain that you understand the problem, and then that you understand each step in the solution. Make clear the units of the physical quantities used and make sure you understand the underlying chemistry. If you have problems, ask.

Always make a note of problems and questions that you need to ask your teacher. Learning is not a contest or a trial. Nobody has ever learnt anything without effort or without running into difficulties from time to time — not even your teachers.

## Notes

Most people have notes of some sort. Notes can take many forms: they might be permanent or temporary; they might be lists, diagrams or flowcharts. You have to develop your own styles. For example, notes that are largely words can often be recast into charts or pictures and this is useful for imprinting the material. The more you rework the material, the clearer it will become.

Whatever form your notes take, they must be organised. Notes that are not indexed or filed properly are useless, as are notes written at enormous length and those written so cryptically that they are unintelligible a month later.

## Writing

In chemistry, you need to be able to write concisely and accurately. This requires you to marshal your thoughts properly and needs to be practised during your day-to-day learning.

Have your ideas assembled in your head before you start to write. You might imagine them as a list of bullet points. Before you write, have an idea of how you are going to link these points together and also how your answer will end. The space available for an answer is a poor guide to the amount that you have to write — handwriting sizes differ hugely, as does the ability to write succinctly. Filling the space does not necessarily mean you have answered the question. The mark allocation suggests the number of points to be made, not the amount of writing needed.

# Content Guidance

# Formulae, equations and amounts of substance

The abilities to calculate formulae from data, write correct formulae, balance equations and perform quantitative calculations are fundamental to the whole study of chemistry. This topic introduces these ideas, and its content could be examined in any unit test.

The ability to lay out calculations in a comprehensible manner depends on:
- knowing what you are doing and not being reliant on rote learning of formulae
- realising that calculations need linking words and phrases to make them readable
- the correct use of units *throughout the calculation*

Using units throughout a calculation is advantageous. It means that you are less likely to get calculations wrong because you are more aware of what you are doing. Some of the advantages are:
- an awareness that equations are not merely symbols, but express relationships between physical quantities
- a check on whether the mathematical expressions used are in fact correct, because of the in-built check on the units of the answer
- a gradual awareness of what sort of magnitude of answer is reasonable in a given set of circumstances

## Some fundamental ideas

- **Atom** — the smallest *uncharged* part of an element, with a central nucleus containing protons and neutrons. The nuclear diameter is about $10^{-4}$ of the atomic diameter. The electrons are located in shells of different energy surrounding the nucleus. The shells are made up of orbitals. The important properties of these three particles are given in the table below:

|  | Mass | | Charge | |
|---|---|---|---|---|
|  | Actual/kg | Relative to proton | Actual/C | Relative to proton |
| Proton | $1.673 \times 10^{-27}$ | 1 | $+1.602 \times 10^{-19}$ | +1 |
| Neutron | $1.675 \times 10^{-27}$ | 1.001 | 0 | 0 |
| Electron | $9.11 \times 10^{-31}$ | 1/1836 | $-1.602 \times 10^{-19}$ | −1 |

- **Atomic number** — the number of protons in an atom.
- **Mass number** — the number of protons plus the number of neutrons in an atom. It is always a whole number.

- **Relative atomic mass** — the average mass (i.e. takes into account the abundance of isotopes in the naturally occurring element) of atoms of an element relative to $\frac{1}{12}$ the mass of a carbon-12 atom, which is defined as 12 exactly.
- **Relative isotopic mass** — the mass of an atom of a particular isotope of an element relative to $\frac{1}{12}$ the mass of a carbon-12 atom, which is defined as 12 exactly.
- **Element** — an element is a substance consisting of atoms that all have the same atomic number.
- **Ion** — an ion is an atom or group of bonded atoms that have lost or gained electrons:
  - Loss of electrons means that there are more protons than electrons in the ion, so the charge is positive and the ion is a cation.
  - Gain of electrons means that there are more electrons than protons in the ion, so the charge is negative and the ion is an anion.
- **Molecule** — a molecule consists of two or more atoms covalently bonded in a fixed ratio to form a single entity.
- **Compound** — a compound is a substance consisting of two or more different types of atoms bonded together in a fixed ratio. If the bonding is covalent — as it is, for example, in water, $H_2O$ — then the compound consists of molecules that are single entities containing the stated number of atoms. If the compound is ionic — for example, sodium chloride — the formula shows the simplest ratio in which the atoms combine. In this example, the formula is NaCl. There are no individual NaCl molecules; there is one sodium ion for every chloride ion in the crystal lattice, but no given pair of ions is special.

> **Examiner tip**
> Relative atomic mass applies to an element and is an average. Relative isotopic mass applies to a single isotope of an element and so is *not* an average.

> **Examiner tip**
> Do not use the words atom and molecule carelessly. Each has its own specific meaning.

# Amount of substance and the Avogadro constant

In chemistry, the term *amount* has a technical meaning. It refers to the number of moles of substance being considered.

A **mole** is that amount of substance that contains the same number of entities as there are atoms in exactly 0.012 kg (12 g) of the isotope $^{12}C$. The entities concerned (molecules, ions, atoms) must also be specified.

The number of entities in a mole of substance is called the **Avogadro constant, $N_A$**. Its value is $6.02214179 \times 10^{23}\,mol^{-1}$.

> **Examiner tip**
> For an ionic solid, such as NaCl, there are $6.02 \times 10^{23}$ $Na^+$ ions and $6.02 \times 10^{23}$ $Cl^-$ ions per mole. For $CaCl_2$ there are $6.02 \times 10^{23}$ $Ca^{2+}$ ions and $2 \times 6.02 \times 10^{23}$ $Cl^-$ ions per mole.

The mole is used because chemistry takes place between particles (molecules, ions or atoms). However, the most convenient way of measuring materials in the laboratory is to weigh them. The Avogadro constant, together with the idea of relative molecular mass, provides the necessary link. Water, $H_2O$, has a relative molecular mass of 18.0. Since 12 g of $^{12}C$ contains (by definition) $N_A$ carbon atoms, it follows that 18 g of water contains $N_A$ water molecules, since every molecule has a mass 18.0/12 times that of a $^{12}C$ atom. In fact, for any molecular substance, its relative molecular mass, in grams, contains $N_A$ molecules of that substance. For an ionic substance, its formula mass, in grams, has $N_A$ formula units. This enables reacting masses to be calculated (see page 13).

> **Knowledge check 1**
> Calculate the number of methane molecules in 0.125 mol of methane.

> **Knowledge check 2**
> Calculate the *total* number of ions in 0.125 mol of aluminium sulfate, $Al_2(SO_4)_3$.

**Molar mass** is the mass (in grams) of a substance that contains $N_A$ molecules or, if ionic, $N_A$ formula units, of the substance. It is numerically the same as the relative molecular (formula) mass of the substance.

**Knowledge check 3**
What is the mass of 1 mol of (a) methane, $CH_4$, (b) sodium chloride, NaCl?

**Knowledge check 4**
Calculate the number of moles in (a) 2.0g of methane, $CH_4$, (b) 2.0g of sodium chloride, NaCl.

# Concentration

The concentration of a solution can be expressed in several ways, each having its own purpose.

The commonest method is to use **mol dm$^{-3}$**, where the concentration is given as the amount of solute per dm$^3$ of *solution*. When solutions are made up, the required amount of solute is measured out and the solvent is then added until the required volume of solution is obtained. It is not possible to predict the volume change when two materials are mixed to give a solution because it depends on how the particles fit together. For example, mixing 50cm$^3$ of water and 50cm$^3$ of ethanol gives only 97cm$^3$ of aqueous ethanol.

It is possible to calculate the mass of a substance in a known volume of a solution of known concentration, as shown below for 50cm$^3$ of sodium hydroxide solution of concentration 0.130mol dm$^{-3}$. Sodium hydroxide has a molar mass of 40g mol$^{-1}$.

$$amount\ of\ NaOH = 0.050\ dm^3 \times 0.130\ mol\ dm^{-3} = 6.5 \times 10^{-3}\ mol$$

$$mass\ of\ NaOH = 6.5 \times 10^{-3}\ mol \times 40\ g\ mol^{-1} = 0.26\ g$$

In solutions that are very dilute and in gases such as air containing some airborne pollutant, the amount of material present is small. In such cases the concentration of the solute is given in **parts of solute per million parts of solvent**, by mass. This is abbreviated to **ppm**. A solution having 1 ppm of solute would have $10^{-6}$g of solute per gram of solution.

# Empirical and molecular formulae

The empirical formula of a compound is its formula in its lowest terms. Therefore, $CH_2$ is the empirical formula of any compound $C_nH_{2n}$, i.e. alkenes, cycloalkanes and poly(alkenes).

The calculation steps give you:
- the moles of each atom
- the ratio of moles of each atom

## Example I

A compound contains 73.47% carbon, 10.20% hydrogen and the remainder is oxygen. The relative molecular mass is 98.0. Find the empirical and molecular formulae of the compound.

### Answer

| | Divide by $A_r$ (= moles) | Divide by smallest (= ratio of moles) | Ratio of atoms |
|---|---|---|---|
| Carbon | 73.47/12.0 = 6.1225 | 6.1225/1.020 = 6 | 6 |
| Hydrogen | 10.20/1.0 = 10.20 | 10.20/1.020 = 10 | 10 |
| Oxygen | 16.33/16.0 = 1.020 | 1.020/1.020 = 1 | 1 |

The compound has the empirical formula $C_6H_{10}O$. The mass of this is:

$$(6 \times 12.0) + (10 \times 1.0) + 16.0 = 98.0$$

So the empirical formula is also the molecular formula.

> **Examiner tip**
> When you use the periodic table, you must be careful to use atomic masses not atomic numbers. For example, carbon is 12.0 not 6.

## Example 2

2.4g of a compound containing carbon, hydrogen and oxygen only was burnt and produced 5.28g of carbon dioxide and 2.88g of water. Calculate the moles of carbon dioxide and water and hence find the empirical formula of the compound.

### Answer

Moles of carbon dioxide = 5.28/44.0 = 0.12 = moles of carbon

Moles of water = 2.88/18.0 = 0.16

Moles of hydrogen = 2 × moles of water = 2 × 0.16 = 0.32

Mass of oxygen in the compound = mass of compound – (masses of carbon and hydrogen) = 2.4 – (5.28 × 12/44.0) – (2.88 × 2/18.0) = 0.64 g

> **Examiner tip**
> If the compound contains oxygen, the mass of oxygen has to be calculated by subtracting the masses of hydrogen and carbon from the mass of the compound.

| Atom | Moles | Divide by smallest (= ratio of moles) | Ratio of atoms |
|---|---|---|---|
| Carbon | 0.12 | 0.12/0.04 = 3 | 3 |
| Hydrogen | 0.32 | 0.32/0.04 = 8 | 8 |
| Oxygen | 0.64/16 = 0.04 | 0.04/0.04 = 1 | 1 |

The empirical formula is $C_3H_8O$.

> **Examiner tip**
> As there are 2 H atoms per molecule in water, the moles of H atoms = 2 × moles of water.

## Example 3

This example shows why you must not do any rounding during the calculation.

A compound contains 39.13% carbon, 52.17% oxygen and 8.70% hydrogen. Calculate the empirical formula.

## Answer

| | Divide by $A_r$ (= moles) | Divide by smallest (= ratio of moles) | Ratio of atoms |
|---|---|---|---|
| Carbon | 39.13/12.0 = 3.26 | 3.26/3.26 = 1 | 1 |
| Oxygen | 52.17/16.0 = 3.26 | 3.26/3.26 = 1 | 1 |
| Hydrogen | 8.70/1.0 = 8.70 | 8.70/3.26 = 2.66 | 2.66 |

The ratios are not whole numbers. This means you have to multiply by a small integer, usually 2 or 3, to get the answer. In this case, multiplying by three gives 3, 3, 8, so the empirical formula is $C_3H_8O_3$.

To find the **molecular formula**, which is the formula of one molecule of the substance, you need additional information such as the molar mass of the compound.

# Chemical equations

The ability to write equations for chemical reactions is important and needs constant practice. Chemical equations, i.e. symbol equations (not word equations which are not equations at all) are central to the language of chemistry.

When writing an equation check that:
- all the formulae are correct
- the equation balances

Whenever you come across a reaction, you should follow these rules:
- learn the equation for it
- check that it balances and make sure that you understand the reason for the presence and amount of each species
- try to visualise what is happening in the reaction vessel

The visualisation of a reaction can be helped by the use of state symbols. The ones commonly used are:
- (s) for solid
- (l) for liquid
- (g) for gas
- (aq) for aqueous solution

It is not always necessary to use state symbols and can be impossible. Thus the reaction between sodium iodide and concentrated sulfuric acid gives a brown mess that contains several substances in a paste with water and acid. Attempts to use state symbols in such cases are not illuminating. However, in the case of thermochemical equations and in equilibria and redox equations, their use is essential.

Chemical equations are not algebraic constructions — they represent real processes. Do not tack atoms or molecules on here and there to make an equation 'balance'; if it does not describe what really happens, it is wrong.

**Knowledge check 7**

Write the equation for the reaction of aluminium with hydrochloric acid to form aluminium chloride and hydrogen

**Examiner tip**

When you write state symbols, make them clear. It is common to find exam scripts where the difference between (s) and (g) is small and not always decipherable.

## Ionic equations

Ionic equations have the advantage that they ignore all the species that are not involved in the reaction (i.e. those that are just 'looking on' as the reaction proceeds — hence the name **spectator ions**).

The rules for writing ionic equations are:

(1) Write out the equation for the reaction.
(2) Separate the *soluble* ionic compounds into their ions.
(3) Leave covalent compounds and insoluble ionic compounds as they are.
(4) Delete the common (spectator) ions from both sides of the equation.

This is illustrated by the reaction between solutions of copper sulfate and sodium hydroxide:

$$CuSO_4(aq) + 2NaOH(aq) \rightarrow Cu(OH)_2(s) + Na_2SO_4(aq)$$

$$Cu^{2+}(aq) + \mathbf{SO_4{}^{2-}(aq)} + \mathbf{2Na^+(aq)} + 2OH^-(aq) \rightarrow$$
$$Cu(OH)_2(s) + \mathbf{SO_4{}^{2-}(aq)} + \mathbf{2Na^+(aq)}$$

The spectator ions are in bold. Deleting these gives the ionic equation:

$$Cu^{2+}(aq) + 2OH^-(aq) \rightarrow Cu(OH)_2(s)$$

**Examiner tip**
Make sure that ionic equations balance for charge.

**Knowledge check 8**
Balance the ionic equation
$Sn^{2+} + Fe^{3+} \rightarrow Sn^{4+} + Fe^{2+}$

# Reacting masses

Equations can be used to find how much material could be produced from given starting quantities.

## Example

Sodium carbonate weighing 5.3 g is reacted with excess hydrochloric acid. Calculate the mass of sodium chloride produced.

## Answer

The molar masses of sodium carbonate and of sodium chloride are needed, since the masses of both are involved in the calculation.

molar mass of $Na_2CO_3 = [(2 \times 23.0) + 12.0 + (3 \times 16.0)]\,g\,mol^{-1} = 106.0\,g\,mol^{-1}$
molar mass of $NaCl = 35.5 + 23.0\,g\,mol^{-1} = 58.5\,g\,mol^{-1}$

Then the steps are:

**Step 1** Calculate the amount of starting material (sodium carbonate), where amount means moles.

**Step 2** Calculate the amount of sodium chloride from the chemical equation.

**Step 3** Calculate the mass of sodium chloride.

The equation is:

$$Na_2CO_3 + 2HCl \rightarrow 2NaCl + CO_2 + H_2O$$

$$\text{amount of } Na_2CO_3 = \frac{5.3\,g}{106.0\,g\,mol^{-1}} = 0.050\,mol$$

amount of NaCl = 2 × 0.050 mol = 0.10 mol

mass of NaCl = 0.10 mol × 58.5 g mol$^{-1}$ = 5.85 g

Most reactions do not give a quantitative yield — there may be competing reactions and there are handling losses unless great care is taken. The **percentage yield** is often calculated and is given by:

$$\% \text{ yield} = \frac{\text{actual yield} \times 100}{\text{calculated yield}}$$

In the example above, an actual yield of 5.21 g sodium chloride would mean a percentage yield of:

$$\frac{5.21 \text{ g} \times 100}{5.85 \text{ g}} = 89\%$$

## Equations from reacting masses

Knowing the mass of the materials that react also gives information about the equation for the reaction. This process was a preoccupation of chemists for much of the eighteenth and nineteenth centuries, since it is the basis on which formulae are determined.

### Example

In a suitable organic solvent, tin metal reacts with iodine to give an orange solid and no other product. In such a preparation, 5.9 g of tin reacted completely with 25.4 g of iodine. What is the formula of the compound produced?

### Answer

molar mass of tin (Sn) = 118.7 g mol$^{-1}$

molar mass of iodine (I) = 126.9 g mol$^{-1}$

amount of tin = $\dfrac{5.9 \text{ g}}{118.7 \text{ g mol}^{-1}}$ = 0.050 mol

amount of iodine atoms = $\dfrac{25.4 \text{ g}}{126.9 \text{ g mol}^{-1}}$ = 0.20 mol

ratio of iodine:tin = 4:1

So, the compound has the empirical formula $SnI_4$.

The data do not tell us whether the compound is $SnI_4$, $Sn_2I_8$ or some other multiple — a molecular mass determination would be necessary to find out. It is actually $SnI_4$.

The calculation in the above example could also be performed in terms of the numbers of atoms of each substance involved. To do this, the amount of each substance has to be multiplied by the Avogadro constant. The answer is the same since $N_A$ cancels during the calculation. This is always true, which is why we use amount of substance, a small number, rather than the number of atoms, which is an extremely large number.

# Calculations involving gas volumes

The molar volume of any gas at a given temperature and pressure is the same. It does not depend on the nature of the gas. At s.t.p., i.e. 0°C and 1 atm pressure, the volume is 22.414 dm³ mol⁻¹. There is no loss of principle in taking it to be 24 dm³ mol⁻¹ at 'room temperature and pressure', but don't forget that this is an approximation.

**Examiner tip**

You must know:

$$\text{moles of gas} = \frac{\text{volume}}{\text{molar volume}}$$

so, at room temperature and pressure,

$$\text{moles of gas} = \frac{\text{volume in dm}^3}{24}$$

or

$$\text{moles of gas} = \frac{\text{volume in cm}^3}{24\,000}$$

**Knowledge check 9**

Calculate the volume of gas, at room temperature and pressure, that contains 0.0246 mol.

The molar volume of a gas can be used to find the volumes of gases obtained from any particular reaction.

## Example 1

This is an extension of the reaction considered previously (page 13).

Sodium carbonate weighing 5.3 g was reacted with excess hydrochloric acid. Calculate the mass of sodium chloride produced and the volume of carbon dioxide obtained at room temperature and pressure.

## Answer

The first steps are as before.

$$Na_2CO_3 + 2HCl \rightarrow 2NaCl + CO_2 + H_2O$$

$$\text{amount of Na}_2\text{CO}_3 = \frac{5.3\,g}{106.0\,g\,mol^{-1}} = 0.050\,mol$$

amount of NaCl = 2 × 0.05 mol = 0.10 mol

mass of NaCl = 0.10 mol × 58.5 g mol⁻¹ = 5.85 g

**Examiner tip**

The equation shows that 2 mol of NaCl are produced from 1 mol of $Na_2CO_3$, so the moles of NaCl will be twice the moles of $Na_2CO_3$.

The volume of $CO_2$ produced is given by the amount multiplied by the molar volume:

amount of $CO_2$ = 0.050 mol

volume of $CO_2$ = 0.050 mol × 24 dm³ mol⁻¹ = 1.2 dm³

## Example 2

50 cm$^3$ of propane was burnt in excess oxygen. What is the volume of carbon dioxide produced?

### Answer

In this case, the substances whose volumes are required are gaseous and the initial volume of propane is given. The volumes are in the same ratio as the amount of each substance in the equation:

$$C_3H_8(g) + 5O_2(g) \rightarrow 3CO_2(g) + 4H_2O(l)$$

molar ratio of the gases propane:carbon dioxide = 1:3

volume of propane = 50 cm$^3$

so, volume of carbon dioxide produced = (3/1) × 50 = 150 cm$^3$

It is not necessary to use the molar volume of the gas.

> **Examiner tip**
>
> This method can only be used if both substances in the question are gases.

## Example 3

27 g of propane was burnt in excess oxygen. What volume of oxygen reacts and what is the volume of carbon dioxide produced?

The molar volume of any gas at the temperature and pressure of the experiment is 24 dm$^3$ mol$^{-1}$.

The molar mass of propane is 44.0 g mol$^{-1}$.

### Answer

$$C_3H_8(g) + 5O_2(g) \rightarrow 3CO_2(g) + 4H_2O(l)$$

amount of propane = $\dfrac{27.0g}{44.0\,\text{g mol}^{-1}}$ = 0.614 mol

amount of oxygen = 0.614 mol × 5 = 3.07 mol

volume of oxygen = 3.07 mol × 24 dm$^3$ mol$^{-1}$ = 73.7 dm$^3$

The volume of carbon dioxide produced is calculated thus:

amount of carbon dioxide = 3 × 0.614 mol = 1.842 mol

volume of carbon dioxide = amount × molar volume

= 1.842 mol × 24 dm$^3$ mol$^{-1}$

= 44.2 dm$^3$

> **Examiner tip**
>
> If the volume of *air* had been asked, the 73.7 dm$^3$ would have to be multiplied by 5, as air is only one-fifth oxygen.

# Percentage yields and atom economies

Until recently, the effectiveness of a synthetic process in chemistry was judged by the percentage yield of the desired compound. Most reactions do not give a quantitative yield — there may be competing reactions, and there will be handling losses unless great care is taken. The percentage yield is given by:

$$\% \text{ yield} = \frac{\text{actual yield of product} \times 100}{\text{calculated yield of product}}$$

With percentage yield, the focus is on the product; the amount of other, possibly useless, materials is not taken into account.

A different measure of the effectiveness of a synthetic process was put forward by Trost (1998). This is the idea of the **atom economy** of a reaction. Atom economy is defined as:

$$\text{atom economy} = \frac{\text{molar mass of the product} \times 100}{\text{molar mass of all the reactants}}$$

### Knowledge check 10

The solvent ethyl ethanoate, $CH_3COOC_2H_5$ can be prepared in two ways:

$CH_3COCl + C_2H_5OH \rightarrow CH_3COOC_2H_5 + HCl$

$CH_3COOH + C_2H_5OH \rightarrow CH_3COOC_2H_5 + H_2O$

Explain which has the higher atom economy.

The better the atom economy, the greater are the proportions of the starting materials that finish up in the product. The advantages of processes with high atom economies are:

- The consumption (and therefore the cost) of starting materials is minimised.
- There is less production of useless materials in the reaction. This becomes increasingly important as the costs of waste disposal and of compliance with stringent disposal regulations rise rapidly.
- Energy costs are often lower.

Reactions can be categorised according to their atom economies:

- Addition reactions have the highest atom economies since all the reactants are consumed in making the product. Examples include addition polymerisation, addition of HBr to alkenes and the hydrogenation of C=C bonds.
- Substitution reactions have lower atom economies, since one group in a molecule is displaced by another, and the displaced material may be of little use. Examples include the reaction, in sulfuric acid solution, of sodium bromide with an alcohol to form a bromoalkane. The products include dilute sodium sulfate, which has no commercial value and is discarded. It is not toxic or dangerous — just useless.
- Elimination reactions have the lowest atom economies since they produce at least two materials from one, and one of these is likely to be of little use. An example is the elimination, using KOH in an ethanol solvent, of HBr from a bromoalkane to give an alkene. The products include potassium bromide in dilute aqueous solution — not particularly problematic, but it does have to be disposed of.

### Examiner tip

The idea of atom economy can be extended to include removal of a product followed by recycling the unused reactants.

After studying this topic, you should be able to:

- define relative atomic mass, relative isotopic mass and atom economy
- calculate the moles of a substance given its mass
- calculate the moles of a gaseous substance given its volume and the molar volume
- calculate the moles of a solute given its concentration and the volume of the solution
- understand the term parts per million (ppm)

- calculate the empirical formulae from % composition or combustion data
- calculate the mass (or volume for gases) of product given the equation for the reaction and the mass (or volume) of a reactant
- calculate the % yield given the mass of a reactant and the product
- calculate the atom economy given the equation

Summary

# Energetics

## Enthalpy change

The heat change ($\Delta H$) that occurs during a chemical reaction at constant pressure (i.e. in a vessel open to the atmosphere) is called the **enthalpy change** for that reaction. It is measured in $kJ\,mol^{-1}$, where '$mol^{-1}$' refers to the molar quantities given in the equation. Therefore:

$$2SO_2(g) + O_2(g) \rightarrow 2SO_3(g) \quad \Delta H = -92\,kJ\,mol^{-1}$$

means that 92 kJ of heat is given out when 2 mol of sulfur dioxide combine with 1 mol of oxygen to give 2 mol of sulfur trioxide. Such an equation is called a **thermochemical** equation.

Note that an enthalpy change should not be called an energy change. Energy changes during reactions are calculated at constant volume and the values obtained are not necessarily the same as the enthalpy change for the reaction.

Changes of state (e.g. from liquid to gas or from solid to liquid) are accompanied by heat changes. The states of the substances in the reaction are important. For example, the combustion of methane would give out more energy if the product water were liquid rather than gaseous, the difference being the enthalpy of vaporisation of the liquid water. Thermochemical equations are commonly shown for substances in their **standard state**, the associated enthalpy changes being standard enthalpies. This is shown by the superscript symbol '$^{\ominus}$', i.e. $\Delta H^{\ominus}$.

Standard conditions mean:
- all reagents and products are in their thermodynamically most stable state
- 1 atmosphere pressure
- a specified temperature — usually 25°C (298 K)

Some elements have different forms (allotropes) in the solid state. For carbon it is necessary to specify graphite or diamond rather than just solid (s).

# Enthalpy level diagrams

Enthalpy level diagrams show the relative energy levels of reactants and products. The horizontal axis is often absent, unlabelled, or may be called the 'reaction coordinate'. Enthalpy level diagrams for exothermic and endothermic reactions are shown below.

**Examiner tip**
Exothermic reactions have a negative value of $\Delta H$.

**Examiner tip**
Always include state symbols in thermodynamic equations.

**Examiner tip**
If a definition of a *standard* enthalpy change is asked, the details of standard conditions must be given in the answer.

**Examiner tip**
Make sure that the arrow for $\Delta H$ goes from the enthalpy level of the reactants to the products.

Heat may be given out or be taken in during a chemical reaction. The international convention is that heat changes are seen from the point of view of the chemical system — imagine you are sitting inside the reaction mixture.

- Heat taken in is regarded as positive; so endothermic processes have a positive $\Delta H$.
- Heat given out is regarded as negative; so exothermic processes have a negative $\Delta H$.

Note that the positive or negative signs represent *conventions* concerning the direction of heat flow. They do not represent relative magnitudes in the same way that plus or minus signs do with numbers. Suppose that for one reaction $\Delta H = -100\,kJ\,mol^{-1}$ and that for another it is $-200\,kJ\,mol^{-1}$. The second value is not smaller than the first — indeed it represents twice as much heat given out. Instead of using the terms 'smaller' or 'larger', which are always ambiguous, use descriptive terms, such as 'more exothermic', or whatever is appropriate.

# Definitions of standard enthalpy changes

- **Standard enthalpy of formation, $\Delta H_f^{\ominus}$**, is the heat change for the formation of 1 mol of substance from its *elements*, all substances being in their most stable state at 1 atm pressure and a specified temperature.
- **Standard enthalpy of combustion, $\Delta H_c^{\ominus}$**, is the heat change when 1 mol of substance is completely burnt in *excess oxygen*, all substances being in their most stable state at 1 atm pressure and a specified temperature.
- **Standard enthalpy of neutralisation, $\Delta H_{neut}^{\ominus}$**, is the heat change when an acid is neutralised by an alkali, to produce *1 mol of water* at 1 atm pressure and a specified temperature.

Strictly speaking, the concentration of the solutions should also be specified when dealing with the standard state, but this refinement is unnecessary for present purposes.

- **Standard enthalpy of atomisation, $\Delta H_{at}^{\ominus}$**, is the heat change for the formation of 1 mol of gaseous atoms from an element in its standard state at 1 atm pressure and a specified temperature.

Note carefully that the definition of $\Delta H_{at}$ refers to the *formation of 1 mol of gaseous atoms*. Therefore, in the case of chlorine, the heat change measured is for the process:

$$\tfrac{1}{2}Cl_2(g) \rightarrow Cl(g)$$

# Some simple thermochemistry experiments

There are several simple experiments that can be used to measure enthalpy changes. The following account is not intended to substitute for worksheets or other practical instructions. For details you should consult a book of practical chemistry. The principles are as follows:

- Use of a known amount of substance.
- Insulation against heat losses. (Although since the temperature rise or fall for most reactions in solution is fairly small, heat losses are much less than is commonly imagined. The same is not true for combustion reactions (e.g. the burning of alcohols to find the heat of combustion), where the heat losses are colossal.

- Correction of the maximum observed temperature change for heat loss or for slowness of reaction. This is particularly important for reactions between solids and liquids (e.g. heat of displacement in the reaction between copper(II) sulfate solution and zinc metal).
- Calculation of the results, using heat change = $mc\Delta\theta$, where $m$ = mass of the liquid that heated up, $c$ = its heat capacity and $\Delta\theta$ the temperature change. $\Delta H$ then equals heat change divided by moles reacted, with a – sign if the temperature rose and a + sign if it fell.

## Determination of enthalpy of neutralisation

*Note*: This technique can also be used for any other type of reaction that can be carried out in an expanded polystyrene cup, so displacement reactions (e.g. between zinc and copper sulfate solution) can also be performed in this way.

The general method for determining the enthalpy of neutralisation is:
- A known volume of acid of known concentration is placed in a polystyrene cup.
- The temperature of the acid is measured for 4 minutes.
- At the fifth minute, a known volume of a solution of a base of suitable concentration is added.
- The temperature is measured every 30 seconds until minute 8.
- A graph of temperature against time is plotted, and the lines are extrapolated to enable the temperature change, $\Delta\theta$, at minute 5, and corrected for any heat losses, to be calculated.

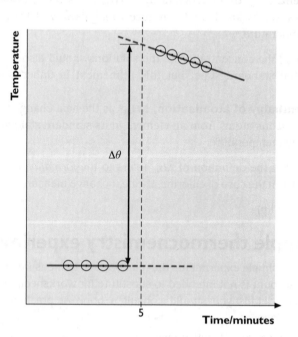

- The heat change ($\Delta H$) is $mc\Delta\theta$, where $m$ is the mass of the solution (usually taken to be equal to its volume for aqueous solutions), $c$ is the heat capacity of the solution (usually taken to be equal to that of water for dilute aqueous solutions), and $\Delta\theta$ is the corrected temperature change.

- The heat change per mole of water formed is then found by dividing the result by the amount (number of moles) of hydrogen ions used.

## Example

When 25.0 cm$^3$ of a 1.00 mol dm$^{-3}$ solution of HCl was added to 25.0 cm$^3$ of 1.10 NaOH the temperature rose by 6.8°C. Calculate the enthalpy change for the neutralisation of hydrochloric acid. [The heat capacity of the solution is 4.18 J °C$^{-1}$ g$^{-1}$.]

## Answer

$$\text{heat produced} = mc\Delta\theta = 50.0\,\text{g} \times 4.18\,\text{J}\,°C^{-1}\,g^{-1} \times 6.8°C = 1421.2\,\text{J}$$

$$\text{amount of HCl} = \text{concentration} \times \text{volume in dm}^3$$

$$= 1.00\,\text{mol dm}^{-3} \times 0.0250\,\text{dm}^3 = 0.0250\,\text{mol}$$

$$\Delta H_{\text{neutralisation}}\text{of HCl} = \frac{-1421.2\,\text{J}}{0.0250\,\text{mol}} = -56.848\,\text{J mol}^{-1} = -56.8\,\text{kJ mol}^{-1}$$

The method of measuring the temperature change is designed to compensate for two sources of error — cooling (or sometimes warming, since some processes are endothermic and the temperature falls below room temperature) and slowness of reaction. The latter is not a problem in finding enthalpies of neutralisation, since all the species are in solution. However, it can be a problem if the reaction is between a solution and a solid.

## Practical details

Using solutions of around 2 mol dm$^{-3}$ concentration results in a temperature rise of about 14°C, which can be measured with reasonable accuracy.

- Measure 30 cm$^3$ of 2.00 mol dm$^{-3}$ hydrochloric acid into an expanded polystyrene cup.
- Measure the temperature of this solution every minute for 4 minutes.
- At the fifth minute, add with stirring 30 cm$^3$ of 2.20 mol dm$^{-3}$ sodium hydroxide solution and measure the temperature every 30 seconds from 5.5 minutes to 8 minutes.
- Plot a graph of temperature ($y$-axis) against time ($x$-axis).
- Extrapolate the lines on the graph to find the corrected temperature change at 5 minutes.

The heat change can then be calculated using $mc\Delta\theta$.

# Enthalpy of combustion of alkanes and alcohols

This simple experiment is not accurate, since the loss of heat to the surroundings is considerable. A set of spirit lamps is used, filled with either a liquid alkane or alcohol.

- A known volume of water is added to a copper calorimeter can.
- The spirit lamp is weighed and placed under the can (without a gauze).
- The temperature of the water is measured and the lamp is lit.
- When the temperature of the water has risen by a suitable amount, the lamp is extinguished and re-weighed.

The heat gained by the water is equal to $mc\Delta\theta$, where $m$ is the mass of water in the calorimeter, $c$ is the heat capacity of water and $\Delta\theta$ is the temperature change. If the mass of the liquid burnt is found from the weighings, then the heat evolved per mole of fuel can be found.

The errors in this experiment are large, arising mainly from the following:
- Heat losses — heat is lost by convection around the calorimeter, so this energy never finds its way into the water.
- Incomplete combustion of the fuel — spirit lamps do not have a good oxygen supply, and the flame, particularly from alkanes, is often sooty.
- Evaporation — some of the fuel evaporates from the spirit lamp, so the mass burnt cannot be determined accurately.

Accurate measurement of combustion enthalpies is carried out using a bomb calorimeter, which is essentially a closed steel vessel containing the fuel with oxygen at high pressure. The calorimeter is completely surrounded by water, so all the heat energy produced on ignition is used to raise the water temperature.

## Hess's law

Hess's law states that the enthalpy change for the process Y → Z is independent of the route used to effect the change, provided that the states of Y and Z are the same for each route.

The use of **standard enthalpies** avoids the problem of the states at the beginning and end of the experiment, since the states of Y and Z are defined.

This means that enthalpy changes can be found using other data. For example, enthalpies of reaction can be found from enthalpies of formation or enthalpies of combustion. It is possible, using Hess's law, to find the enthalpy change for reactions that cannot be performed directly.

*Note*: Hess's law is a particular case of the first law of thermodynamics, which states that matter can be neither created nor destroyed.

## Using enthalpies of formation

The Hess's law diagram for calculating enthalpy of reaction from enthalpies of formation is shown below.

Hess's law says that C = A + B, where A, B and C are the enthalpy changes. Using the definition of enthalpies of formation:

A = − (sum of the enthalpies of formation of the reactants)

B = (sum of the enthalpies of formation of the products)

Therefore:

C = (sum of the enthalpies of formation of the products) −

(sum of the enthalpies of formation of the reactants)

Consider the combustion of ethanol:

$$CH_3CH_2OH(l) + 3O_2(g) \rightarrow 2CO_2(g) + 3H_2O(l)$$

The example shows how the heat change for the combustion of ethanol can be found. The states of all substances must be shown, because changes of state also involve enthalpy changes.

$$\Delta H_c^\ominus = 2\Delta H_f^\ominus(CO_2) + 3\Delta H_f^\ominus(H_2O) - \Delta H_f^\ominus(CH_3CH_2OH)$$

Inserting the appropriate values gives:

$$\Delta H_c^\ominus = 2(-393.5) + 3(-285.8) - (-277.1) = -1367.3 \, kJ\,mol^{-1}$$

Note that oxygen is not included, as it is an element in its standard state.

## Using enthalpies of combustion

The Hess's law diagram for calculating enthalpy of reaction from enthalpies of combustion is shown below.

A = (sum of the enthalpies of combustion of the reactants)

B = − (sum of the enthalpies of combustion of the products)

Therefore:

C = A + B = (sum of the enthalpies of combustion of the reactants) −
(sum of the enthalpies of combustion of the products)

Consider the reaction between ethanol and ethanoic acid to give ethyl ethanoate and water:

$$CH_3CH_2OH(l) + CH_3COOH(l) \rightarrow CH_3COOCH_2CH_3(l) + H_2O(l)$$

The Hess's law diagram for this reaction using enthalpies of combustion is shown below:

$$\Delta H_r^\ominus = \Delta H_c^\ominus(CH_3CH_2OH(l)) + \Delta H_c^\ominus(CH_3COOH(l)) - \Delta H_c^\ominus(CH_3COOCH_2CH_3(l))$$

Water, of course, does not burn. Inserting the appropriate values gives:

$$\Delta H_r^\ominus = (-1367.3) + (-874.1) - (-2237.9) = -3.5 \, kJ\,mol^{-1}$$

## Using mean bond enthalpies

Hess's law can be used to find approximate values of $\Delta H^{\ominus}$ for a reaction by use of mean bond enthalpies. The **mean bond enthalpy** is the enthalpy change when 1 mol of the specified type of bond is broken; an average value is taken which has been determined over a wide variety of molecules. This is the reason why it is approximate — bond enthalpies may vary quite a lot. Thus the C=O bond enthalpy in $CO_2$ is 805 kJ mol$^{-1}$ but in methanal, HCHO, it is 695 kJ mol$^{-1}$. Breaking all the bonds in all the reactants leads to a collection of atoms; thus polyatomic elements such as oxygen have to be included in the calculations, unlike in the case of enthalpies of formation.

The Hess's law diagram for the use of bond enthalpies is shown below:

```
                    Atoms
            A    ↗       ↘    B
                              
  Reactants ───────────────→ Products
                     C
```

A = (sum of bond enthalpies of the reactants)

B = –(sum of the bond enthalpies of the products)

Therefore:

C = (sum of bond enthalpies of the reactants) –
                              (sum of the bond enthalpies of the products)

**Bond enthalpies are always endothermic, i.e. positive.**

When working out enthalpies of reaction from bond enthalpies, use the following rules:

- Write the reaction using structural formulae, so that you remember all the bonds.
- Ignore groups that are unchanged between the reactants and the products. In the addition reaction of ethene with hydrogen, there is no need to involve the $CH_2$ groups since they survive unchanged. There is no point in breaking all the bonds only to make them again.

### Knowledge check 14

Use bond energies on page 13 of the Edexcel data booklet (or other data source) to calculate the enthalpy change of the reaction:

$H_2C=CHCH_3 + HCl \rightarrow CH_3CHClCH_3$

Consider, again, the combustion of ethanol:

The bonds broken are 5 C–H, 1 C–C, 1 C–O (note the single bond) and 1 O–H. Those made are 4 C=O (note the double bond) and 6 O–H. Use the equation presented above, together with the bond enthalpies from the Edexcel data booklet (or other data source) to calculate the approximate enthalpy of reaction.

| Bonds broken | Value/kJ mol⁻¹ | Bonds made | Value/kJ mol⁻¹ |
|---|---|---|---|
| $5 \times$ C–H | $5 \times 413 = 2065$ | $4 \times$ C=O | $4 \times -805 = -3220$ |
| $1 \times$ C–C | 347 | $6 \times$ O–H | $6 \times -464 = -2784$ |
| $1 \times$ C–O | 358 | | |
| $1 \times$ O–H | 464 | | |
| Total | 3234 | Total | −6004 |

**Examiner tip**
The value for $\Delta H$ is only approximate as *average* bond enthalpies were used in the calculation.

approximate $\Delta H$ of reaction $= 3234 - 6004 = -2770 \, \text{kJ mol}^{-1}$

# Experiments on enthalpy changes for reactions that cannot be performed directly

Many Hess's law calculations relate to reactions that cannot be performed directly. For such reactions, knowledge of the enthalpy change, $\Delta H$, is useful in other contexts.

For example, the direct determination of $\Delta H$ for the decomposition of sodium hydrogencarbonate on strong heating is not possible. The reaction is:

$$2NaHCO_3(s) \rightarrow Na_2CO_3(s) + CO_2(g) + H_2O(g)$$

An approximate method for finding $\Delta H$ is to react sodium hydrogencarbonate and sodium carbonate separately with hydrochloric acid, finding the heat change in each case. The two values obtained can be combined to give an approximate value for $\Delta H$. It is not the actual value because the states of the various reagents are not exactly the same as in the thermal decomposition, but, if desired, adjustments can be made for this using other data, such as hydration enthalpies and enthalpies of solution.

A known amount of sodium hydrogencarbonate is reacted with an excess of hydrochloric acid in an expanded polystyrene cup and the temperature change is determined using methods described previously (page 20). A similar experiment using sodium carbonate is performed and $\Delta H$ for each reaction is calculated.

Equation I: $NaHCO_3(aq) + HCl(aq) \rightarrow NaCl(aq) + CO_2(g) + H_2O(l)$    $\Delta H_1$

Equation II: $Na_2CO_3(aq) + 2HCl(aq) \rightarrow 2NaCl(aq) + CO_2(g) + H_2O(l)$    $\Delta H_2$

The overall thermal decomposition reaction approximates to $(2 \times$ equation I$) -$ (equation II), so that:

$$\Delta H = 2\Delta H_1 - \Delta H_2$$

**Knowledge check 15**

Use the enthalpies of solution of hydrated and anhydrous copper(II) sulfate

$CuSO_4.5H_2O(s) \rightarrow CuSO_4(aq)$    $\Delta H = +6 \, \text{kJ mol}^{-1}$

$CuSO_4(s) \rightarrow CuSO_4(aq)$    $\Delta H = -73 \, \text{kJ mol}^{-1}$

to calculate the enthalpy change for:

$CuSO_4.5H_2O(s) \rightarrow CuSO_4(s) + 5H_2O(l)$

# Bond enthalpies and reaction mechanisms

## Reaction of halogenoalkanes with hydroxide ions

The rate of reaction between the halogenoalkanes and hydroxide ions in aqueous ethanol depends on the bond strength of the carbon–halogen bond, all other things being equal. If X is a chlorine, bromine or iodine atom:

$$CH_3CH_2X + OH^- \rightarrow CH_3CH_2OH + X^-$$

The average bond enthalpy of C–Cl is $346 \, kJ \, mol^{-1}$, of C–Br is $290 \, kJ \, mol^{-1}$, and of C–I is $228 \, kJ \, mol^{-1}$.

When chloro-, bromo- and iodoethane are placed separately in solutions of silver nitrate in aqueous ethanol and left in a warm-water bath, the precipitate of silver iodide appears first, followed by that of silver bromide and then, after a much longer time, silver chloride. The stronger the carbon–halogen bond, the slower the reaction, as the activation energy for the reaction increases in the order iodo- < bromo- < chloro-.

### Examiner tip

The rate of reaction is determined by the C–X bond energy and *not* by its polarity.

## Photohalogenation of methane with chlorine.

The overall equation for this reaction is:

$$CH_4(g) + Cl_2(g) \rightarrow CH_3Cl(g) + HCl(g)$$

The initiation step is:

$$Cl_2 \rightarrow 2Cl\bullet$$

This is followed by one of two possible propagation steps:

Possible step I: $CH_4 + Cl\bullet \rightarrow \bullet CH_3 + HCl$

Possible step II: $CH_4 + Cl\bullet \rightarrow CH_3Cl + H\bullet$

We can use bond enthalpies to predict which propagation step is the more likely:
- Possible step I — a C–H bond is broken ($+435 \, kJ \, mol^{-1}$) and an H–Cl bond made ($-432 \, kJ \, mol^{-1}$), giving $\Delta H = +3 \, kJ \, mol^{-1}$
- Possible step I — a C–H bond is broken ($+435 \, kJ \, mol^{-1}$) and a C–Cl bond is made ($-346 \, kJ \, mol^{-1}$), giving $\Delta H = +89 \, kJ \, mol^{-1}$

Step I, being less endothermic, is the more likely. This is supported by the observed products — step II would give rise to some hydrogen as a result of two H• radicals combining, but none is seen, whereas step I would lead to some $C_2H_6$ forming as a result of two •$CH_3$ radicals colliding.

## Summary

After studying this topic, you should:
- know that $\Delta H$ values for exothermic reactions are negative
- know that when the temperature of a reaction mixture rises, $\Delta H$ will be negative
- be able to draw enthalpy level diagrams of exo and endothermic reactions.

- be able to define the standard enthalpy of:
  - formation
  - combustion
  - neutralisation
  - atomisation
- be able to calculate $\Delta H$ of a reaction using:
  - experimental data
  - Hess's law
  - mean bond enthalpies

# Atomic structure and the periodic table

For most purposes the atom is regarded as having a central nucleus containing protons (charge of +1 and mass of 1) and neutrons (charge of zero and mass slightly higher than 1). The diameter of the nucleus is about $10^{-5}$ of the atomic diameter. The electrons are located in shells of different energy levels surrounding the nucleus. The shells are made up of orbitals.

## Definitions

- **Atomic number** — the number of protons in an atom.
- **Mass number** — the number of protons plus the number of neutrons.

**Examiner tip**
The relative isotopic mass is nearly the same as the mass number for a given atom; for carbon-12 it is exactly the same. The difference arises because the neutron and the proton do not have exactly the same mass, and because mass is lost (as energy) when the nucleons come together to form the nucleus. This energy is called the binding energy of the nucleus.

- **Isotopes** – atoms having the same proton number but different mass numbers. They have the same electronic structure and therefore the same chemistry. They differ only in mass.
- **Relative isotopic mass** — the mass of a particular isotope of an element, relative to $1/12$ the mass of a carbon-12 atom.
- **Relative atomic mass** — the mean of the masses of the atoms of the element relative to $1/12$ the mass of a carbon-12 atom. For chlorine, which is 75% $^{35}Cl$ and 25% $^{37}Cl$, the relative atomic mass is $(0.75 \times 35) + (0.25 \times 37) = 35.5$.
- **Relative molecular mass** — the mass of a molecule relative to $1/12$ the mass of a carbon-12 atom. For an ionic compound, this quantity is sometimes called the relative formula mass.

## The mass spectrometer

The mass spectrometer can be used to determine relative atomic mass. It works as follows:
- Gaseous samples of elements or compounds are bombarded with high-energy electrons.
- This causes ionisation, producing positive ions.
- These ions are accelerated by an electric field.
- They are then bent by a magnetic field into a circular path whose radius depends on their mass.
- A detector enables the number of ions at each particular mass to be determined.

The resulting mass spectrum gives information about the isotopic composition of elements or structural information about compounds.

**Examiner tip**
Do not forget the *positive* charge when giving the formula of a species causing a peak in a mass spectrum.

The spectrum of ethanol, $CH_3CH_2OH$, showing the major fragment ions, is given below:

Uses of mass spectral data include:

- determination of the isotopic composition of an element. This was first achieved for neon, when F. W. Aston showed the presence of $^{10}Ne$ and $^{11}Ne$, thus discovering that isotopes exist.

**Knowledge check 16**

Bromine has two stable isotopes, $^{79}Br$ and $^{81}Br$. Explain how many peaks due to the $Br_2^+$ ion will be seen in its mass spectrum.

- deduction of the relative atomic mass of an element. This involves finding the masses and abundances of the isotopes, as shown above in the calculation for chlorine on page 27.
- deduction of the structure of an organic compound from the masses of the molecular ions and the fragments that arise from bombardment of the molecules.
- determination of the relative molecular mass of a compound, provided that the molecular ion is present. Not all compounds give a molecular ion peak.
- measurement of the $^{14}C$:$^{12}C$ ratio in the radioactive dating of organic material. The older the material, the smaller this ratio is. This application (known as carbon dating) showed that the flax used to make the Turin Shroud, supposedly the burial shroud of Jesus, was grown within a few years of 1305.
- identification of molecules in blood and urine. This application is used on samples taken from athletes for drug testing.

# Ionisation energy and electron affinity

## Ionisation energy

The **first ionisation energy** for an atom is the energy change involved in the removal of one electron from each of a mole of atoms in the gas phase, i.e. the energy change per mole for:

$$E(g) \rightarrow E^+(g) + e^-$$

The general trend *across a period* is an increase in first ionisation energy. This is because there is a greater attraction between the outer electrons and the nucleus, which is caused by:

- an increase in the number of protons
- the outer electrons being shielded to approximately the same extent by the inner electrons
- the atoms being smaller

There are two discontinuities. One is between groups 2 and 3 where the outer electron is now in the higher *p*-orbital. Another discontinuity is between groups 5 and 6 where the electron removed is from the *p*-orbital and is repelled by the other electron in that orbital.

The first ionisation energies decrease down a group. The number of protons increases, but so does the number of shielding electrons. However, the outer electrons are in a shell further from the nucleus and so are attracted less strongly.

The **second ionisation energy** is the energy change per mole for:

$$E^+(g) \rightarrow E^{2+}(g) + e^-$$

Successive ionisation energies are defined similarly.

Successive ionisation energies show the existence of quantum shells; there are significant jumps in ionisation energy between each shell. Thus, for aluminium there is a big jump between the third and fourth ionisation energies, as the fourth electron has to be removed from the inner second shell.

Elements of groups 1 and 2 have *s*-electrons as their outer electrons and constitute the *s*-block; those of groups 3 to 0 have outer *p*-electrons and constitute the *p*-block. In the *d*-block, the *d*-sub-shell is being filled — for example, $_{21}$Sc to $_{30}$Zn are *d*-block elements. However, the outer electrons for these elements are *s*-electrons.

**Knowledge check 17**

Complete the electron configuration of (a) silicon and (b) manganese using the 1s, 2s... notation.

The electron energy levels fill in the following order as atomic number rises as far as krypton (element 36): $1s$, $2s$, $2p$, $3s$, $3p$, $4s$, $3d$, $4p$. The electrons enter the next sub-shell, once the previous one is full. Thus, $_{23}V$ has the electron configuration $1s^2$, $2s^2$, $2p^6$, $3s^2$, $3p^6$, $4s^2$, $3d^3$.

## Orbitals

Chemistry is concerned with elements bonding together, which involves electrons. The electronic structure therefore determines the chemistry of an element.

The electrons in atoms do not orbit the nucleus like planets around the sun. They exist as volumes of electron density — the **orbitals** — centred on the nucleus. In orbitals, electrons remain unpaired as far as possible, so, for example, $p^3$ represents one electron in each of the three $p$-orbitals.

Section through s-orbital          One p-orbital

The $s$-orbital is a sphere centred on the nucleus; each of the three $p$-orbitals (one along each axis) is rather like two balloons at 180°. Covalent bonds are formed by the overlap of orbitals on different atoms, usually one electron each, to give a molecular orbital which can be represented by an electron-density map. This maps the density from the pair of electrons that form the bond.

## Electron affinity

The **first electron affinity** of an atom is the energy change for addition of one electron to each of a mole of atoms in the gas phase:

$$X(g) + e^- \rightarrow X^-(g)$$

This is exothermic, since the electron is attracted to the nuclear charge.

**Examiner tip**

It is always a good idea to add an equation to definitions of ionisation energy and electron affinity, with X representing the element.

The **second electron affinity** is the energy change per mole for

$$X^-(g) + e^- \rightarrow X^{2-}(g)$$

This is endothermic, since the incoming electron is repelled by the negative charge on the ion.

## Periodic properties

The reason that elements in the same group have similar properties is that some properties recur periodically. Ionisation energy is one example, as shown in the graph for period 2 (elements 3–10) and period 3 (elements 11–18) (see page 29). Thus, all the alkali metals have low ionisation energies; the noble (inert) gases have high ionisation energies.

The melting and boiling temperatures of the elements of periods 2 and 3 also show periodic trends. The values for the metals in groups 1–3, with strong metallic bonding, are much higher than those for the non-metals in groups 5–0, but are comparable with those of the giant covalent structures of the group 4 elements carbon and silicon, which have many covalent bonds between the atoms and so a very high melting temperature.

The melting and boiling temperatures of an element reflect the binding energies in the crystal or liquid states. In metals, this depends on the size of the ions, their charge and the number of delocalised electrons. The metallic radii in period 3 are larger than those in period 2, so the metals have lower melting and boiling temperatures. With the elements in group 5–0, the more electrons in the molecule, the greater are the van der Waals forces (covered in Unit 2) and the higher the melting and boiling temperatures.

Periodic trends are shown in the table below.

| Element | Li | Be | B | C (graphite) | N | O | F | Ne |
|---|---|---|---|---|---|---|---|---|
| Melting temp./°C | 181 | 1278 | 2300 | 3697 | −210 | −218 | −220 | −248 |
| Boiling temp./°C | 1342 | 2970 | 2550 | 4827 | −196 | −183 | −188 | −246 |
| Structure | Body-centred cubic | Hexagonal close packing | Tetrahedral | Giant molecule | $N_2$ | $O_2$ | $F_2$ | Atoms |

| Element | Na | Mg | Al | Si | P | S | Cl | Ar |
|---|---|---|---|---|---|---|---|---|
| Melting temp./°C | 98 | 649 | 660 | 1410 | 44 | 119 | −101 | −189 |
| Boiling temp./°C | 883 | 1107 | 2467 | 2055 | 280 | 445 | −35 | −186 |
| Structure | Body-centred cubic | Hexagonal close packing | Face-centred cubic | Giant molecule | $P_4$ (white phosphorus) | $S_8$ | $Cl_2$ | Atoms |

After studying this topic, you should be able to:
- define atomic and mass numbers
- define isotopes
- define relative atomic and isotopic masses
- define ionisation energy
- define electron affinity
- explain how a mass spectrometer works
- deduce the relative atomic mass from mass spectra data
- state the electron configuration of elements up to $_{38}Sr$
- explain the trends in first ionisation energies across a period and in a group
- explain the trends of melting temperatures of elements in a period

**Summary**

# Bonding

## Ionic bonding

### The formation of ions

An **ionic bond** is the attraction between a positive and a negative ion.

- Positive ions or **cations** are formed by loss of electron(s) from atoms or groups of atoms. The ions are usually metal ions, but can be non-metallic — for example, the ammonium ion, $NH_4^+$.
- Negative ions or **anions** are formed when atoms or groups of atoms gain electrons.
- The ions formed may have octets of electrons, but many $d$-block metal ions do not. The ion that forms gives the strongest bonding in a resulting compound.
- The driving force for ion formation lies in the lower energy of the compound formed, compared with the constituent elements.

### Evidence for the existence of ions

The evidence for the existence of ions in compounds comes from electrolysis. The passage of a current through a molten salt or aqueous salt solution relies on the movement of the ions, which then lose electrons at the anode or gain them at the cathode to form the constituent elements.

This movement can be seen if the ions are coloured. Copper(II) chromate, $CuCrO_4$, contains blue $Cu^{2+}$ and yellow $CrO_4^{2-}$ ions. If a small crystal is placed at the middle of a strip of wetted filter paper attached at each end to a power supply, a yellow colour spreads to the positive electrode and a blue colour to the negative electrode.

### Ionic crystals

An ionic crystal consists of a giant three-dimensional lattice of ions. The structure depends on the relative size of the anion and cation, and on the stoichiometry of the substance. Clearly, NaCl (shown below) cannot have the same crystal structure as $MgCl_2$.

The crystal is held together by a *net* attractive force between oppositely charged cations and anions. There are also longer-range repulsive forces between ions of the same charge. However, because these ions are more widely separated the repulsive forces are not as large as the attractive forces between ions of different charge. Because the attractive forces are uniform over the whole crystal:

- ionic substances have high melting and boiling temperatures
- there are no individual molecules in the solid that have the formula of the crystal (e.g. NaCl) — the formula simply shows the relative proportions of the ions in the crystal

The attractive force between two ions is described by Coulomb's law:

Na⁺
Cl⁻

$$|F| = \frac{Q_1 Q_2}{k(r_+ + r_-)^2}$$

where $|F|$ is the magnitude of the force between the ions, $Q_1$ and $Q_2$ are the charges on the two ions, $k$ is a constant, and $r_+ + r_-$ is the sum of the radii of the two ions and is, therefore, the distance between the centres of the ions when they are touching in the crystal. For a given crystal structure, the attractive force depends on the product of the two charges, and inversely on the square of the distance between the ion centres.

Formation of an octet alone does *not* make an ion more stable than the atom from which it arose (see the Born–Haber cycles below).

## Ionic radii

Metal ions (cations), formed by electron loss, are smaller than the metal atoms from which they arose. This is because, in forming an ion, the metal atom loses its outer electron shell.

A non-metal ion formed from a single atom is similar in size to the atom. The addition of extra electron(s) to the outer shell (which already contains electrons) makes little difference to the size. Polyatomic anions, such as sulfate $SO_4^{2-}$, are much larger.

**Knowledge check 20**

Explain why an $O^{2-}$ ion is bigger than an $F^-$ ion.

The size of ions increases going down a group in the periodic table. Successive members of the group have one more shell of electrons. They also have more protons in the nucleus. The combined effect of more shells and more attraction from the nucleus means that size does increase, but not as dramatically as might be expected:

| Group 1 | Li | Na | K | Rb | Cs |
|---|---|---|---|---|---|
| Atomic radius/nm | 0.157 | 0.191 | 0.235 | 0.250 | 0.272 |
| Ionic radius (+1 ion)/nm | 0.074 | 0.102 | 0.138 | 0.149 | 0.150 |

| Group 7 | F | Cl | Br | I |
|---|---|---|---|---|
| Atomic radius/nm | 0.155 | 0.180 | 0.190 | 0.195 |
| Ionic radius (−1 ion)/nm | 0.133 | 0.180 | 0.195 | 0.215 |

**Isoelectronic ions** are ions that have the same electron configuration.

Because their nuclei are different, they are different ions. There are six ions that have the electron configuration $1s^2\, 2s^2\, 2p^6$. Their radii (in nm) are shown in the table below:

| $N^{3-}$ | $O^{2-}$ | $F^-$ | $Na^+$ | $Mg^{2+}$ | $Al^{3+}$ |
|---|---|---|---|---|---|
| 0.171 | 0.140 | 0.133 | 0.102 | 0.072 | 0.053 |

The decrease in ionic radius from nitrogen to aluminium is due to the increasing positive charge on the nucleus, which pulls the electron shells closer in.

## Born–Haber cycles

The formation of an ionic crystal from its elements can be broken down into a series of stages for which the energy changes can be measured. This enables calculation of the **lattice energy**, which, since it is a measure of the attraction between the ions, is a measure of how strongly the crystal is bonded.

**Lattice energy** is the energy change for the formation of 1 mol of ionic solid from its isolated gaseous ions.

The lattice energy cannot be measured directly; if an ionic crystal is heated it might vaporise or it might decompose before it does so.

The vapours of ionic materials do not contain separate ions, but rather ion pairs. Thus, gaseous sodium chloride is $Na^+Cl^-$, and the energy needed to form ion pairs is not the same as the lattice energy.

However, there are other processes for which the energy change can be measured and which, when put together in a Born–Haber cycle, enable a value for the lattice energy to be calculated. Such values are called **experimental values**. The lattice energy can also be calculated from the geometry of the crystal and the use of Coulomb's law, which gives a value for the **theoretical lattice energy**, or the lattice energy for a *purely* ionic model. Actual lattice energy and theoretical lattice energy are seldom the same, because most ionic crystals also have some covalent bonding.

The Born–Haber cycle for sodium chloride is shown below:

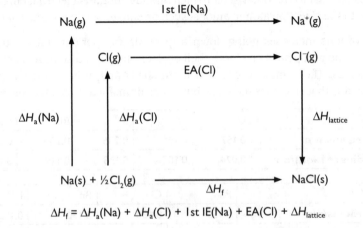

$$\Delta H_f = \Delta H_a(Na) + \Delta H_a(Cl) + 1st\ IE(Na) + EA(Cl) + \Delta H_{lattice}$$

## Polarisation of ions: covalence in ionic lattices

Ionic and covalent bonds are extremes. Ionic bonds involve complete electron transfer and covalent bonds involve equal sharing of electrons. In practice, bonding in most compounds is intermediate between these two forms, with one type being predominant.

The attraction that a bonded atom has for electrons is called its **electronegativity**. There are several electronegativity scales, the commonest being the Pauling scale. Fluorine is the most electronegative element with a value of 4, caesium the least at 0.7.

- Atoms with the same electronegativity bond covalently, with equal sharing of electrons.
- Atoms with different electronegativities form polar covalent bonds if the difference is not too large — up to about 1.5 — and ionic bonds if the difference is more than about 2.

Cations are able to distort the electron clouds of anions, which are generally larger. This leads to a degree of electron sharing and hence some covalence in most ionic compounds. Small cations with a high charge (2+ or 3+) have a high charge density. They can polarise anions, and therefore have a high **polarising power**. Large anions do not hold on to their outer electrons very tightly, so they can be easily distorted — such ions are **polarisable**.

The effect of polarisation is that the lattice energy of these compounds is different from that predicted on the basis of a purely ionic model; the lattice energy is more exothermic, so the lattice is stronger. The smaller the cation associated with a given anion, the greater is the degree of covalency. This is because smaller cations have higher charge densities.

| Compound | $\Delta H_{latt}/kJ\,mol^{-1}$ (ionic model) | $\Delta H_{latt}/kJ\,mol^{-1}$ (Born–Haber) | Difference/kJ mol⁻¹ |
|---|---|---|---|
| $MgCl_2$ | −2326 | −2526 | 200 |
| $CaCl_2$ | −2223 | −2258 | 35 |
| $SrCl_2$ | −2127 | −2156 | 29 |
| $BaCl_2$ | −2056 | −2033 | 23 |

The larger the anion associated with a given cation, the greater is the degree of covalency. This is because the larger anions are more polarisable.

**Knowledge check 22**
Put the following in order of increasing difference between experimental and theoretical lattice energies:
$NaCl$  $MgBr_2$  $MgCl_2$

| Compound | $\Delta H_{latt}/kJ\,mol^{-1}$ (ionic model) | $\Delta H_{latt}/kJ\,mol^{-1}$ (Born–Haber) | Difference/kJ mol⁻¹ |
|---|---|---|---|
| $MgF_2$ | −2913 | −2957 | 44 |
| $MgCl_2$ | −2326 | −2526 | 200 |
| $MgBr_2$ | −2097 | −2440 | 343 |
| $MgI_2$ | −1944 | −2327 | 383 |

# Why $MgCl_2$ rather than MgCl or $MgCl_3$?

The crystal formed from magnesium and chlorine is that which maximises the lattice energy. It has the formula $MgCl_2$.

It is true that less energy is needed to form $Mg^+$ than is needed to form $Mg^{2+}$. However, the 2+ ion has lost an electron shell and is half the size of the $Mg^+$ ion. Thus, the 2+ cation can approach the chloride anion more closely. It also has double the charge of $Mg^+$. Taken together, these two factors make the lattice energy increasingly exothermic. The attraction of $Mg^{2+}$ for the chloride anion is, therefore, much greater than that of $Mg^+$ and so the lattice energy for $MgCl_2$ ($-2526\,kJ\,mol^{-1}$) is much more exothermic than that for MgCl (estimated at about $-700\,kJ\,mol^{-1}$).

$MgCl_3$ would require the formation of $Mg^{3+}$, which is $7733\,kJ\,mol^{-1}$ more endothermic than the formation of $Mg^{2+}$, but with hardly any change in size. The attraction of $Mg^{3+}$ for the chloride ion is not sufficiently greater than the attraction of $Mg^{2+}$ for the extra ionisation energy to be recovered by an increase in lattice energy.

**Knowledge check 23**
Why is sodium chloride not $NaCl_2$?

# Covalent bonding

**Examiner tip**

Covalent bonds are *not* broken when a molecular covalent substance, such as water, is melted or boiled.

A **covalent bond** is the attraction between two nuclei and a shared pair of electrons.

Covalent bonds are strong and have a number of features:
- Electrons are shared in pairs.
- A bond is formed by the overlap of two orbitals.
- Two or three electron pairs can be shared between a pair of atoms to give a double or triple bond.
- The bonded atoms often contain octets but some have only six electrons in the valence (outer) shell — for example, in $BCl_3$ there are only six electrons round the boron atom. Atoms in period 3 and beyond can have more than eight electrons since $d$-orbitals are available — for example, S in $SF_6$ has 12 electrons in the valence shell.

**Knowledge check 24**

State the number of electrons in the outer orbit of a phosphorus atom in $PCl_5$.

- Dative covalent bonds are formed when both bonding electrons come from the same atom.
- Dative bonds are no different from any other covalent bond.
- Dative bonds are found in $NH_4^+$; between chlorine and electron-deficient aluminium in $Al_2Cl_6$; and as the bonds between water ligands and the central metal ion in hexaqua ions of metals such as $[Mg(H_2O)_6]^{2+}$ and $[Fe(H_2O)_6]^{2+}$.
- Electrons do not 'circle around' nuclei — they exist as charge clouds or orbitals. Covalent bonds consist of overlapping orbitals. Ordinary covalent bonds are overlapping one-electron orbitals, whereas dative bonds are from overlap of a two-electron orbital with an 'empty' orbital.

**Knowledge check 25**

Draw how the 1s orbital of hydrogen overlaps with a 3p orbital of chlorine when forming a molecule of HCl.

Giant atomic structures such as diamond and graphite illustrate the strength of covalent bonds:
- All the bonds in the diamond crystal are covalent. It has layers of hexagonal rings that are puckered (i.e. not flat); each carbon atom is bonded covalently to four others throughout the lattice. A great deal of energy is needed to break these bonds, so diamond has an extremely high melting temperature (about 3800°C). There are no free electrons, so diamond is a poor electrical conductor. It is a good thermal conductor, since the rigid lattice readily transmits vibrations.
- Graphite has layers of flat hexagons with a fourth bond delocalised along the plane of the carbons. The forces between the layers are van der Waals forces and are, therefore, weak. Graphite is really a stack of giant molecules, rather like a pile of paper. It is a good electrical conductor parallel to the planes of carbon atoms, but a poor thermal conductor. It sublimes at 3730°C.

**Knowledge check 26**

Why does oxygen have a very much lower melting point than either diamond or graphite?

Covalent compounds that are small molecules have strong bonds *between atoms* — intramolecular bonds — but much weaker forces *between molecules*. They have, therefore, low melting and boiling temperatures because little energy is required to overcome the **intermolecular forces** between molecules.

## Electron density maps

The electron density map for a molecule shows the electron density per unit volume as a set of contours. The map for hydrogen is shown below, with electron density increasing the nearer the contour is to the nucleus. The covalent bond forms because the electron density envelops both atoms.

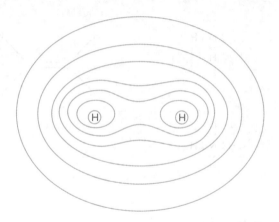

In ionic compounds, the electron densities from the cation and the anion are separate, as in sodium chloride. The chloride ions are larger than the sodium ions. The electron density map for sodium chloride is shown below:

## Dot-and-cross diagrams

The electron structure of a covalent molecule can be drawn as a dot-and-cross diagram (Lewis structure), in which the electron pairs are shown as dots and crosses. The electrons are of course identical, so a diagram with all dots or all crosses would also be a correct representation. Some examples are shown below.

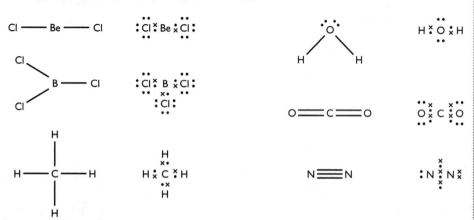

H——N——H          H $\overset{\times}{\underset{\bullet\times}{\cdot}}$ N $\overset{\times}{\cdot}$ H
    |                 •×
    H                 H

          H——N——H

    H
    |
H——N——H          H $\overset{\times}{\cdot}$ N $\overset{\times}{\cdot}$ H
    |                 ו
    H                 H

## Metallic bonding

The Drude–Lorentz model of a metallic crystal shows the following features:

- Metal ions are usually held in a close-packed lattice, the exception being group 1 metals, which are not close-packed.
- The outer (valence) electrons are delocalised throughout the metal crystal.
- The bonding is not particularly directional. This means the lattice can be distorted without breaking, so the metal is malleable and ductile.
- The delocalised electrons are mobile and enable conduction of electricity in the solid.
- The more delocalised electrons there are, the stronger the bonding and the higher the melting temperature.
- The smaller the metal ion, the closer the packing and the higher the melting temperature is.

**Examiner tip**

Metals conduct electricity by movement of *electrons*, whereas ionic compounds conduct, when molten only, by movement of *ions*.

**Knowledge check 28**

Explain why magnesium has a higher melting temperature than sodium.

**Summary**

After studying this topic, you should be able to:

- explain an ionic bond, a covalent bond, a dative covalent bond and a metallic bond
- give evidence for the existence of ions
- explain why ionic compounds have high melting temperatures
- explain why the lattice energy of NaCl is more exothermic than that of KCl

- calculate the lattice energy from Born–Haber data
- explain why theoretical and experimental lattice energies may differ
- draw dot-and-cross diagrams for covalent molecules
- explain why metals conduct electricity and why potassium has a lower melting temperature than calcium

# Introductory organic chemistry

## Introduction

Organic chemistry is dominated by a number of **homologous series**, arising from the presence of one or more functional groups (see below) in a molecule. The huge variety of organic compounds arises from the fact that organic chemistry is rather like atomic Lego, as you will realise if you've used molecular model kits.

**Examiner tip**
All organic compounds burn in excess air to form carbon dioxide and water.

## Homologous series

A homologous series is a series of compounds that:
- have a common general formula
- differ by $CH_2$
- show a trend in physical properties, for example boiling temperature
- show similar chemical properties since all members of the same homologous series have the same functional group

The first member of a homologous series often shows differences in the detail of its chemistry from successive members of the series.

The **alkenes** are an example of a homologous series in that:
- their general formula is $C_nH_{2n}$ (though not all compounds with this general formula are alkenes)
- they have a C=C double bond (which other compounds with the same general formula do not have)
- there is no alkene with only one carbon atom since there could not be a C=C bond

The first three straight-chain compounds in the series are ethene, $CH_2=CH_2$, propene, $CH_3CH=CH_2$, and butene. Butene has structural and geometric isomers (see below), one of which is but-1-ene, $CH_2=CHCH_2CH_3$. The boiling temperatures of these three alkenes are $-104°C$, $-47.7°C$ and $-6.2°C$ respectively. All three react rapidly with bromine water, with potassium manganate(VII) solution, and with all the other reagents given on pages 52–53.

## Functional groups

A **functional group** is a small group of atoms or perhaps a single atom that determines the chemistry of a molecule. The homologous series and functional groups appropriate to AS and A2 are given in the table below. R represents an organic group.

**Examiner tip**
The functional groups are shown by the atoms in bold.

| Series | General formula | First member |
|---|---|---|
| Alkanes | $C_nH_{2n+2}$ | $CH_4$, methane |
| Alkenes | $C_nH_{2n}$ | $CH_2=CH_2$, ethene |
| Halogenoalkanes | R**X** where **X** is –Cl, –Br or –I. | $CH_3Cl$, chloromethane (or bromo- or iodo-) |

| Series | General formula | First member |
|---|---|---|
| Primary alcohols | RCH$_2$OH | CH$_3$OH, methanol |
| Secondary alcohols | RR'CHOH where R and R' may be the same | CH$_3$CH(OH)CH$_3$, propan-2-ol |
| Tertiary alcohols | RR'R"COH where the Rs may be the same | (CH$_3$)$_3$COH, 2-methylpropan-2-ol |
| Aldehydes | RCHO | HCHO, methanal |
| Ketones | RCOR' R and R' can be the same | CH$_3$COCH$_3$, propanone |
| Carboxylic acids | RCOOH | HCOOH, methanoic acid |
| Acid chlorides | RCOCl | CH$_3$COCl, ethanoyl chloride |
| Esters | RCOOR' R and R' can be the same. R, but not R', can be H. | HCOOCH$_3$, methyl methanoate |
| Primary amines | RNH$_2$ | CH$_3$NH$_2$, aminomethane |

**Knowledge check 29**

Identify the functional groups in CH$_3$CH(OH)CH$_2$CH=CH$_2$.

# Naming and drawing organic compounds

In organic chemistry, the structure of a compound is central to its chemistry. All but rather simple molecular formulae give rise to a variety, sometimes enormous, of different structures.

## Nomenclature

The International Union of Pure and Applied Chemistry (IUPAC) has generated a series of rules giving organic compounds **systematic names.** Knowing the rules and the systematic name of a compound means the formula can be written, and vice versa.

The names may be long if the compounds are large. Systematic names are used in the Edexcel specification for most organic substances, though there are exceptions, for example the amino acid, glycine. However systematic names are less common in chemistry beyond school level. This is partly because American textbooks and chemical suppliers do not often use them and partly because the names are unwieldy if more than five or six carbon atoms are involved.

The rules for naming alkanes are given below, with some examples. These rules are built on to name other types of organic molecule.

- Identify the longest carbon chain — take care with this since structures can be written with 90° bond angles that may mask the longest chain. Thus the following compound has a four-carbon longest chain, not three carbons.

$$CH_3 - CH_2$$
$$|$$
$$CH_3 - CH - CH_3$$
$$|$$
$$CH_3$$

- The name is based on the alkane with the same number of carbon atoms as the longest chain.
- Substituent groups have the name ending changed to -yl.

This is illustrated for alkanes up to $C_5$ in the table below.

| C | Alkane | Name stem | Substituent group | Structure |
|---|--------|-----------|-------------------|-----------|
| 1 | Methane, $CH_4$ | Meth- | Methyl | $CH_3-$ |
| 2 | Ethane, $C_2H_6$ | Eth- | Ethyl | $CH_3CH_2-$ |
| 3 | Propane, $C_3H_8$ | Prop- | Propyl | $CH_3CH_2CH_2-$ |
| 4 | Butane, $C_4H_{10}$ | But- | Butyl | $CH_3CH_2CH_2CH_2-$ |
| 5 | Pentane, $C_5H_{12}$ | Pent- | Pentyl | $CH_3CH_2CH_2CH_2CH_2-$ |

- The position of each substituent group is indicated by a number. This corresponds to the position in the chain of the carbon atom to which it is attached, so that the number of the substituent group is the lowest possible. However, for substances such as carboxylic acids, RCOOH, where the functional group is at the end of a chain, the carbon atoms are always numbered from that end.

> **Knowledge check 30**
>
> Name the compound shown in this diagram.

- Different series of compounds have the name-ending modified to indicate which homologous series is involved.
- Where two groups that are the same are substituted on a given carbon atom, the number is repeated and the substituent is prefixed 'di'.
- Where two groups that are the same are on different carbon atoms, 'di' is still used; if there are three groups the same on different carbons then 'tri' is used; if there are four groups then 'tetra' is used, and so on.

**Knowledge check 31**

Name $CH_3CH=C(CH_3)$ $CH(CH_3)CH_2CH_3$.

## Examples of systematic names

### Alkanes

$$CH_3CH_2CHCH_3$$
with $CH_3$ branch

2-methylbutane

$$CH_3CCH_2CHCH_3$$
with $CH_3$, $CH_3$ and $CH_3$ branches

2,2,4-trimethylpentane

### Alkenes

The position of the double bond (or bonds) is given by the number of the carbon atom that the double bond starts from.

$CH_3CH=CH_2$
Propene

$CH_3CH_2CH=CH_2$
But-1-ene

$CH_3CH=CHCH_3$
But-2-ene

$CH_2=CH-CH=CH_3$
Buta-1,3-diene; not an alkene, but an alkadiene

### Halogenoalkanes

$CH_3CH_2CH_2Cl$
1-chloropropane

$BrCH_2CH_2Br$
1,2-dibromoethane

$CH_3CHCH_3$ with $Br$ branch
2-bromopropane

### Alcohols

$CH_3CH_2CH_2OH$
Propan-1-ol

$HOCH_2CH_2OH$
Ethane-1,2-diol

$CH_3CHCH_3$ with $OH$ branch
Propan-2-ol

### Aldehydes

$CH_3CH_2CH_2CHO$
Butanal

$CH_3CHCH_2CH_2CHO$ with $CH_3$ branch
4-methylpentanal

### Ketones

$CH_3COCH_3$
Propanone

$CH_3COCH_2CH_2CH_3$
Pentan-2-one

$CH_3CH_2COCH_2CH_3$
Pentan-3-one

## Carboxylic acids

CCH₃CH₂CH₂COOH
**Butanoic acid**

CH₂=CHCOOH
**Propenoic acid**

CH₃CH=CH₂COOH
**But-2-enoic acid**

CH₃CH₂COOH
**Propanoic acid — note the difference**

CH₃CHCH₂COOH
|
OH
**3-hydroxybutanoic acid**

HOOC–COOH
**Ethanedioic acid**

## Drawing organic molecules

The molecular formula of an organic compound may not be particularly useful, since there is usually more than one possible structure — for example, $C_4H_{10}$ has three possible structures. This problem is overcome by presenting formulae in different ways:

- **Structural formulae** show most of the structure, but not all of the bonds are shown. The side-chain substituents are shown in parentheses.
- **Displayed formulae** show all of the bonds.
- **Skeletal formulae** are used widely for natural products and other large molecules. They show the carbon skeleton by lines (which represent the bonds joining the atoms), but do not show the carbon and hydrogen atoms. All other types of atom are shown.

Consider the molecule 2-methylbutane. Four representations of its structure are shown in the diagram below:

CH₃CH(CH₃)CH₂CH₃

**Structural formula**

CH₃
|
CH₃CHCH₂CH₃

**Semi-displayed formula**

**Displayed formula**

**Skeletal formula**

The example of *cis*-but-2-enoic acid illustrates how to represent C=C double bonds and atoms other than carbon:

CH₃CH=CHCOOH

**Structural**

**Displayed**

**Skeletal**

# Safety in practical chemistry: hazard and risk

Safety is important in chemistry for obvious reasons. Chemistry nevertheless deals with compounds that may be hazardous, so that part of a chemist's training is in the safe use of hazardous materials. **Hazard** is not the same as **risk** — to take a simple example of the difference, a deep lake with treacherous currents is a hazard, but it poses no risk unless you happen to be on it or in it. Hazard is an intrinsic property; risk is personal.

In any question on safety, you would be expected to suggest safety precautions specific to the experiment under consideration, and to be able to assess which is the most significant of various hazards presented.

In this context, the use of lab coats, safety glasses and pipette fillers is considered routine good practice and does not receive credit in examination answers.

The following is presented so as to give you the idea of the basis on which risk assessments might be made. *Safety will not be examined in this detail.* However, comments made by students on safety matters tend to be either so trivial as to be not worth reading, or so apocalyptic as to suggest that all chemistry should cease forthwith.

Every experiment should be the subject of a risk assessment by the institution that intends to perform it.

## Hazard evaluation

The **hazard** associated with a substance is its potential to impair health. Some degree of hazard can be ascribed to almost any substance, while for some the toxicity or the harmful effects are not known fully.

Substances that are likely to be hazardous are those that are
- flammable — almost all organic substances
- carcinogenic materials — benzene
- toxic — barium salts, ethanedioic acid, halogens
- corrosive — concentrated sulfuric acid
- irritant — hydrogen chloride vapour

You may be asked to evaluate the risks in an experiment and state how you would minimise these risks.

## Exposure potential

Hazardous substances vary enormously in potency. A substance with a high hazard may therefore present an acceptably small risk if the exposure potential is low. Conversely, unacceptable risks may result from high exposures to substances with low hazard.

Factors to be taken into account in evaluating exposure potential relate to both **substance** and **activity**.

Substance factors include:
- quantity used — small quantities reduce the risk
- volatility — very volatile organic substances increase the possibility of fire

**Knowledge check 32**

You are required to warm a boiling tube containing the volatile solvent ether, $C_2H_5OC_2H_5$. What is the main hazard in doing this and how would you minimise the risk?

- concentration if in solution — dilute acids are less corrosive than concentrated acids

Small-scale working is preferred wherever possible as this reduces the risk when using hazardous materials.

An alternative method using less hazardous materials should be used wherever possible.

## Flammable substances

Flammable substances must be kept away from naked flames, so any heating necessary must be with a hot-water bath (not heated from underneath by a Bunsen burner) or an electric heating mantle.

## Common hazards in school chemistry

The following list is by no means exhaustive or definitive.

**Halogens** are toxic and harmful by inhalation, although iodine is less toxic than chlorine or bromine, because it is a solid. Chlorine and bromine must always be used in a fume cupboard. Liquid bromine causes serious ulcerating burns and must be handled with gloves, so is best left to demonstration experiments by the teacher.

**Ammonia** is toxic. Concentrated ammonia solutions should be handled in the fume cupboard.

**Concentrated mineral acids** are corrosive. If spilt on the hands, washing with plenty of water — *never* alkali, which is even more damaging — is usually enough, but advice must be sought. Acid in the eye requires *immediate* and copious irrigation and immediate professional medical attention.

**Barium chloride solution** is extremely poisonous, as are **chromates** and **dichromates**.

**Sodium hydroxide, potassium hydroxide** or **concentrated ammonia** in the eye is *extremely serious*, and must always receive professional and *immediate* medical attention following copious irrigation of the eye. Sodium hydroxide and other alkali metal hydroxides are among the most damaging of all common substances to skin and other tissue. Treat them with respect.

**Phenol** is damaging to skin and should always be handled with gloves.

School chemistry laboratories possess data sheets on the hazards associated with chemicals. They may have CLEAPSS hazard cards produced specifically for schools; otherwise, every chemical supplier sends hazard data with any chemical that has been ordered.

None of the above is intended to prevent people doing chemistry — it is intended to encourage safe working practices.

In summary, risk can be minimised by:
- heating very flammable substances with a water bath or electric heating mantle
- wearing gloves when using corrosive substances
- carrying out experiments that involve toxic vapours in a fume cupboard

> **Knowledge check 33**
>
> You have been asked to investigate the reaction between concentrated sulfuric acid and solid sodium bromide, which produces bromine vapour. What are the hazards and how would you reduce the risks?

- working on a smaller scale
- carrying out the reaction using an alternative method that involves less hazardous substances

# Alkanes

- **Alkanes** (also known as the paraffins) are hydrocarbons — compounds that contain hydrogen and carbon *only*.
- Their molecules are saturated — they contain only single bonds.
- They form a homologous series, with the general formula $C_nH_{2n+2}$.

The first four alkanes in the series have names that are unrelated to the number of carbon atoms:
- methane, $CH_4$
- ethane, $CH_3CH_3$
- propane, $CH_3CH_2CH_3$
- butane, $CH_3CH_2CH_2CH_3$

For alkanes with five or more carbon atoms, the names are related to the number of carbon atoms in the chain: pentane, hexane, heptane, octane etc.

## Structural isomerism

**Structural isomers** are compounds that have the same molecular formula but different structural formulae. The first three alkanes, $CH_4$, $CH_3CH_3$ and $CH_3CH_2CH_3$, have only one possible structure in each case. However the fourth, $CH_3CH_2CH_2CH_3$, has a structural isomer in which the atoms are arranged differently:

$$CH_3CH_2CH_2CH_3 \qquad\qquad CH_3CHCH_3$$
$$\qquad\qquad\qquad\qquad\qquad\qquad\qquad\qquad | $$
$$\text{Butane} \qquad\qquad\qquad\qquad CH_3$$

2-methylpropane

In the case of the alkanes, the structural isomers are also alkanes.

However, structural isomers may be of different types. Thus, the molecular formula $C_2H_6O$ could represent ethanol, $CH_3CH_2OH$, or the totally different methoxymethane, $CH_3OCH_3$, which is an ether. This is sometimes called **functional group isomerism**.

Pentane has two structural isomers, so there are three structures that have the molecular formula $C_5H_{12}$:

**Knowledge check 34**

Draw the skeletal formulae of the three isomers of molecular formula $C_5H_{12}$.

$$CH_3CH_2CH_2CH_2CH_3 \qquad CH_3CHCH_2CH_3 \qquad\qquad\quad CH_3$$
$$\qquad\qquad\qquad\qquad\qquad\qquad\qquad\qquad | \qquad\qquad\qquad\qquad\quad |$$
$$\qquad\qquad\qquad\qquad\qquad\qquad\qquad CH_3 \qquad\qquad CH_3CCH_3$$
$$\qquad\qquad\qquad\qquad\qquad\qquad\qquad\qquad\qquad\qquad\qquad\qquad\quad |$$
$$\qquad\qquad\qquad\qquad\qquad\qquad\qquad\qquad\qquad\qquad\qquad\qquad\quad CH_3$$

Pentane  \qquad\qquad  2-methylbutane  \qquad\qquad  2,2-dimethylpropane

The number of structural isomers rises rapidly with the number of carbon atoms in the compound, as illustrated in the table below:

| Alkane | Number of isomers |
|---|---|
| $C_8H_{18}$ | 18 |
| $C_{10}H_{22}$ | 75 |
| $C_{12}H_{26}$ | 355 |
| $C_{14}H_{30}$ | 1858 |
| $C_{20}H_{42}$ | 366 319 |
| $C_{25}H_{52}$ | 36 797 588 |
| $C_{30}H_{62}$ | 4 111 846 763 |
| $C_{40}H_{82}$ | 62 491 178 805 831 |

**Examiner tip**
Because the number of potential structures can be large (even for small compounds), you should always use the structural formula to eliminate ambiguity.

# Fuels

Fuels are obtained from the **fractional distillation** of crude oil. This process usually produces too little of the petrol and diesel fractions and too much of the heavier fuel and lubricating oil fractions. The latter are passed over suitable catalysts, with heating, in order to crack (or break) the molecules into smaller alkanes. Cracking also produces important alkenes used for chemical synthesis, which are too valuable to burn.

## Liquid and gaseous fuels

The advantages and disadvantages of liquid and gaseous fuels depend on:
- whether the fuel has to be carried with the device using it (as in motor vehicles) or whether it can be piped (as in domestic gas supplies)
- any safety aspects peculiar to the particular fuel, especially the handling of potentially explosive gases (these do not include flammability, which some exam candidates seem to think is a problem — the idea of non-flammable fuels is weird!)
- the energy yield per unit volume or unit mass (shown in the table below)

| Fuel | $M_r$ | $\Delta H_c/kJ\,mol^{-1}$ | $\Delta H_c/kJ\,cm^{-3}$ | $\Delta H_c/kJ\,g^{-1}$ |
|---|---|---|---|---|
| Hydrogen(g) | 2 | −286 | −0.012 | −143 |
| Methane(g) | 16 | −890 | −0.037 | −55.6 |
| Butane (g) | 58 | −2877 | −0.12 | −49.6 |
| Butane(l) | 58 | −2877 | −29.8 | −49.6 |
| Octane(l) | 114 | −5470 | −33.8 | −48.0 |
| Ethanol(l) | 46 | −1367 | −23.4 | −29.7 |

(The molar volume of the gases is taken as $24\,dm^3$.)

### Hydrogen and methane

Hydrogen and methane have a high energy yield per gram, but are not dense and therefore large volumes of gas are needed. They are used where the fuel can be piped to the point of use.

Hydrogen can be used in cars — it is compressed and adsorbed in a suitable metal sponge. However, the range of such vehicles is limited and the relatively heavy gas canisters take up a lot of space. There are presently few hydrogen filling stations.

All gaseous fuels present special handling requirements to avoid leakage of flammable or explosive gases. However, these problems have been solved.

**Environmental factors** Hydrogen burns to give water only. Remember, though, that the means of producing hydrogen (electrolysis of brine or reaction of methane with steam) consumes energy, so the environmental advantages of burning hydrogen have to be balanced by the various costs of its production. Methane is used in fixed systems and is burned efficiently, so that little carbon monoxide pollution results.

### Butane

Butane has a high energy yield per gram, but the gas is not dense. It is easily liquefied by compression to give liquefied petroleum gas (LPG). Butane can be used in cars that are adapted for it — the number of filling stations selling it is rising. It is also used in tanks and cylinders as a constituent of Calor gas. The liquid form vaporises readily and requires special handling facilities.

### Octane

Octane has a high energy yield per gram and is the densest of the fuels listed. Therefore, manageable volumes of the fuel can be carried in motor vehicles. It is universally available. The liquid is volatile, but not so volatile that special handling is needed.

**Environmental factors** The yield of carbon monoxide from internal combustion engines is high. Most of this can be removed by the use of catalytic converters, in which carbon monoxide reacts with the nitrogen oxides that are also produced, to give nitrogen and carbon dioxide.

### Ethanol

Ethanol has a high energy yield per gram, but it is not as dense as octane. Therefore, larger volumes of liquid are needed compared with octane. Ethanol is made from oil, if that is available, so it is not a cost-effective fuel for countries that have relatively cheap oil. Countries such as Brazil that have no oil but have a lot of sugar cane can make cheap, fuel-grade ethanol by fermentation. Car fuel in Brazil contains 20% ethanol and 80% ordinary petrol.

**Environmental factors** Ethanol is a clean fuel, producing little carbon monoxide.

## Reactions of alkanes

### Reaction with oxygen

In a plentiful supply of oxygen or air, alkanes burn on ignition to give carbon dioxide and water. The reactions are strongly exothermic, hence the use of alkanes as fuels:
- Methane is natural gas:
$$CH_4 + 2O_2 \rightarrow CO_2 + 2H_2O + heat$$
- Petrol is a mixture that can be represented by octane:
$$C_8H_{18} + 12\tfrac{1}{2}O_2 \rightarrow 8CO_2 + 9H_2O + heat$$

The main constituent in petrol is actually 2,2,4-trimethylpentane, which is an isomer of octane. In internal combustion engines, *complete* combustion does not occur; carbon and carbon monoxide are produced as well as carbon dioxide. In limited oxygen, all of the hydrogen in a given molecule is always oxidised — hydrogen is *never* a product.

## Reaction with chlorine or bromine

In the presence of ultraviolet (UV) light, alkanes react with chlorine or bromine to give halogenoalkanes. In strong UV or focused sunlight the reaction is explosive.

The reaction involves **radical substitution**. There is a mixture of products, because radicals (in this case halogen atoms) are reactive and reactions with the first halogenoalkane produced occur, resulting in further substitution. Methane reacting with chlorine gives $CH_3Cl$ initially, which reacts to give, successively, $CH_2Cl_2$, $CHCl_3$ and $CCl_4$. Direct halogenation is not a good way of making single compounds, but is useful for making solvents, which can be mixtures.

$$CH_4 + Cl_2 \rightarrow CH_3Cl + HCl$$

$$CH_4 + Br_2 \rightarrow CH_3Br + HBr$$

A **substitution reaction** is where one atom or group replaces another in a molecule. There are always two reactants and two products.

### Free radical substitution

The **mechanism** of a reaction is a way of representing how electrons are moved from the reactants to form the products. There are seven types of mechanism studied at AS and A2. The halogenation of alkanes involves **free radical substitution**; it is also a **chain reaction**.

Curly arrows are used to show the movement of electrons. They must be drawn with precision. The tail of the arrow must come from the electron(s); the head must be where the electrons go, to form a bond, radical or ion. The movement of a single electron is shown by a half-headed arrow; that of an electron pair by a full-headed arrow.

A **radical** is an atom or group of atoms with an unpaired electron.

Most radicals are very reactive.

The first step in the chlorination of methane produces chlorine radicals (atoms), the Cl–Cl bond having been broken by UV light. The single electron is shown as a dot. This type of bond breaking, in which one electron from the bond goes to each of the fragments produced, is called **homolytic fission**.

**Examiner tip**
Half-headed arrows should be shown in the initiation step.

The first **initiation step** produces the chlorine radicals:

$$Cl \quad\widehat{\phantom{x}}\widehat{\phantom{x}}\quad Cl \longrightarrow 2Cl\bullet$$

The feature of a chain reaction is that the **propagation steps** that follow initiation produce one radical for every radical consumed. A chlorine radical attacks the methane molecule, producing a methyl radical and hydrogen chloride:

$$CH_4 + Cl\bullet \rightarrow HCl + \bullet CH_3$$

**Examiner tip**
Do *not* think that $CH_3Cl$ and H$\bullet$ are formed in the first propagation step.

The methyl radical then attacks a chlorine molecule, to give chloromethane and a chlorine radical:

$$\bullet CH_3 + Cl_2 \rightarrow CH_3Cl + Cl\bullet$$

The chlorine radical attacks a methane molecule, and so the chain is propagated.

There are several possible **termination steps** where two radicals react to form a molecule, but not further radicals, thus ending the chain propagation:

$$\bullet CH_3 + \bullet CH_3 \rightarrow C_2H_6$$

$$\bullet CH_3 + Cl\bullet \rightarrow CH_3Cl$$

$$Cl\bullet + Cl\bullet \rightarrow Cl_2$$

The mechanism for the bromination of methane is similar.

## Alkenes

Alkenes are a homologous series with the general formula $C_nH_{2n}$. An alkene also contains a C=C double bond. Because of this double bond, alkenes are **unsaturated** compounds.

The double bond consists of two bonds that are not identical. Head-on overlap of carbon $p$-orbitals gives a σ-bond, in which the electron density is coaxial with the C–C internuclear axis. There is also sideways overlap between $p$-orbitals on the carbon atoms, which gives a π-bond as the other part of the double bond. The σ-bond is shorter than in saturated compounds (e.g. ethane), so is somewhat stronger; the σ-bond component accounts for about two-thirds of the overall strength of the C=C bond.

### Geometric isomerism

**Geometric isomerism** results from restricted rotation about a carbon–carbon double bond, provided that the groups on a given carbon in the C=C bond are not the same.

Thus in the diagram above 'a' and 'e' must be different, as must 'b' and 'd'. The groups do not *all* have to be different from one another. The diagram below shows two geometric isomers:

These are *cis-* and *trans-*1,2-dichloroethene. In *cis-*isomers the substituent groups, in this case the same, are on the same side of the C=C bond.

**Examiner tip**

The presence of ethane as a minor product is evidence for this mechanism.

**Examiner tip**

Anything that prevents rotation, such as a ring of carbon atoms, could cause geometric isomerism. Thus 1,2-dichlorocyclohexane exists as two geometric isomers.

**Knowledge check 35**

Explain why but-1-ene, $CH_2=CHCH_2CH_3$, does not show geometric isomerism.

Sideways overlap of the *p*-orbitals to give a π-bond means that there is no rotation about C=C bonds, except at high temperatures.

## The E–Z system of naming geometric isomers

If there are only two substituents (other than hydrogen) on the C=C bond, the *cis–trans* naming system works well. In the case of compounds that have more than two different groups around the C=C bond — for example, 2-bromobut-2-ene, the two forms of which are shown below — it is better to name them using a different system.

A            B

The rules are based on those of Cahn, Ingold and Prelog for naming chiral compounds. The substituent groups are ordered in a priority determined by the atomic mass of the atom directly bonded to a carbon atom. Taking isomer **A** above, hydrogen has atomic mass 1.0 and carbon has atomic mass 12.0. Thus, the carbon in the methyl group has the higher priority on the left-hand carbon. On the right-hand carbon, bromine (atomic mass 79.9) has higher priority than carbon (atomic mass 12.0). The two high-priority substituents are, therefore, the methyl ($CH_3$) group and the bromine, which are on opposite sides of the C=C bond. This isomer is the *entgegen* isomer, or *E*-isomer.

In isomer **B**, the high-priority groups are on the same side of the C=C bond, therefore, this is the *zusammen* or *Z*-isomer.

In fact, 2-bromobut-2-ene could be named using the *cis–trans* nomenclature; isomer **A,** with the methyl groups on the same side, being the *cis*-isomer. If one of these methyl groups were changed to an ethyl group then it would not be possible to assign *cis*- or *trans*- to the isomers. If all four groups are different as in F and G below:

F            G

then only the *E–Z* system will work. You should convince yourself that **F** is the *Z*-isomer.

If the groups get larger (e.g. ethyl or propyl), the rules are extended to the masses of the groups attached to the doubly bonded carbon atoms.

**Knowledge check 36**

Draw the skeletal formula of the *E*-isomer of 3-methylpent-2-ene.

# Addition reactions

Propene $CH_3CH=CH_2$ is a good example, since it is an unsymmetrical alkene, i.e. the substituents on each end of the C=C bond are not the same. This is significant in some reactions.

An **addition reaction** is where two substances form a single substance.

## Reaction with hydrogen

Propene reacts with hydrogen at room temperature in the presence of a platinum catalyst, or at 150°C with a nickel catalyst, to give propane:

$$CH_3CH=CH_2 + H_2 \rightarrow CH_3CH_2CH_3$$

This particular reaction is not useful industrially — alkenes are far more valuable than alkanes, since they are more reactive. However, it is the basis of margarine manufacture, and reduction of C=C bonds in more complex molecules is often required.

## Reaction with halogens

Propene reacts with chlorine or bromine in the gas phase, or in an inert solvent (e.g. $CCl_4$), at room temperature:

$$CH_3CH=CH_2 + Br_2 \rightarrow CH_3CHBrCH_2Br$$

The product is 1,2-dibromopropane. The brown bromine is decolourised.

The reaction of bromine water (aqueous bromine) with alkenes is used to test for the presence of a C=C bond — the orange bromine water is decolourised. BrOH is added, not bromine itself:

$$CH_3CH=CH_2 + HOBr \rightarrow CH_3(Br)CHCH_2OH$$

**Examiner tip**

The HOBr is formed by the reaction of bromine with water:

$$Br_2 + H_2O \rightarrow HOBr + HBr$$

## Reaction with hydrogen halides

Propene reacts with hydrogen bromide in the gas phase, or in an inert solvent, at room temperature to form 2-bromopropane as the major product, with some 1-bromopropane.

$$CH_3CH=CH_2 + HBr \rightarrow CH_3CHBrCH_3$$

The mechanism is **electrophilic addition**.

The hydrogen goes to the carbon atom in the double bond that already has the most hydrogen atoms on it. This is Markovnikoff's rule; this 'rule' is *not* an explanation and there are exceptions to it. It is, however, a useful guide. The reasons for the orientation are dealt with on page 54, when considering the mechanism.

Hydrogen chloride and hydrogen iodide react with propene in a similar manner to hydrogen bromide.

## Reaction with potassium manganate(VII) solution

Propene reacts with potassium manganate(VII) solution, whether acidic (in $H_2SO_4$), neutral or alkaline (in $Na_2CO_3$), to give propane-1,2-diol:

$$CH_3CH=CH_2 \xrightarrow{KMnO_4} CH_3CH(OH)CH_2OH$$

The precise nature of this reaction is still not known, so a balanced equation is not written. The purple $KMnO_4$ solution is usually converted to a brown sludge of $MnO_2$.

## Mechanisms

### Electrophilic addition of bromine to ethene

### Electrophilic addition of hydrogen bromide to ethene

## Content Guidance

### Electrophilic addition of hydrogen bromide to propene

Secondary carbocation — major

Primary cation — minor. In the secondary carbocation intermediate, the $C^+$ is stabilised by the electron-pushing effect of a $CH_3$ group. Thus it is more likely to be formed than the primary carbocation, which does not have a $CH_3$ group attached to the $C^+$.

fast

2-bromopropane — major product

fast

1-bromopropane — minor product

> **Knowledge check 37**
>
> Write down the formula of the major product of the reaction of HCl(g) with 2-methylbut-2-ene.

## Polymerisation of alkenes

**Polyalkenes** are made by radical addition reactions. A radical initiator such as a peroxide or oxygen is heated with the alkene. The first step is dissociation of the initiator into radicals:

$$R \underset{}{\overset{}{-\!\!-}} R \longrightarrow 2R\bullet$$

The radical then attacks the alkene to form a new radical, and so on:

$$R\bullet \quad H_2C = CH_2 \longrightarrow RCH_2 \overset{\bullet}{-\!\!-} CH_2$$

$$RCH_2 \overset{\bullet}{-\!\!-} CH_2 \quad H_2C = CH_2 \longrightarrow RCH_2CH_2CH_2 \overset{\bullet}{-\!\!-} CH_2$$

Because radicals are very reactive, they can attack growing chains at any point, forming branches and cross-links between the chains. The reaction stops when two radicals combine. Polymers contain molecules with a wide variety of chain lengths, so they soften over a range of temperatures rather than melting sharply.

Alkene monomers can contain substituent groups other than hydrogen. These groups *never* form part of the central carbon chain. This is illustrated in the table below:

| Monomer | Polymer | Name |
|---|---|---|
| $CH_2=CH_2$ | $-\!\!\left(CH_2-CH_2\right)_{\!n}\!-$ | Poly(ethene) |
| $CH_2=CHCH_2$ | $-\!\!\left(CH_2-\overset{\displaystyle \mid}{\underset{\displaystyle CH_3}{CH}}\right)_{\!n}\!-$ | Poly(propene) |
| $CH_2=CHCl$ | $-\!\!\left(CH_2-\overset{\displaystyle \mid}{\underset{\displaystyle Cl}{CH}}\right)_{\!n}\!-$ | Poly(chloroethene), PVC |
| $CF_2=CF_2$ | $-\!\!\left(CF_2-CF_2\right)_{\!n}\!-$ | Poly(tetrafluoroethene), PTFE |

## Polymers and resources

Polymers are made from oil and need energy for their manufacture. They are unreactive. There are many different varieties that are not always easily distinguishable. Burning polymers can give rise to toxic fumes. With the exception of PTFE, polymers are cheap.

Wrapping food in polymers has improved its keeping quality and has, therefore, reduced food waste and the incidence of food-related illness. In some cases, paper products could be used instead of polymers — unlike oil, paper is a renewable resource. However, the energy consumption in paper manufacture is significant. It also requires considerable quantities of water, the supply of which can be more of a problem than finding suitable trees — most of these are grown as a crop. Paper is never made from tropical hardwoods, so it does not contribute to rainforest decline; it is made from the timber of conifers. The soil in which conifers are grown emits nitrogen oxides into the atmosphere and can contribute a greater volume of nitrogen oxides to the locality than motor vehicles do. So, paper cups are not necessarily better than poly(styrene) ones.

All these points have to be borne in mind when using polymer products or considering alternatives. Polymers can all be recycled, but recycling has energy costs in terms of transport and reprocessing of a low-value material. Sorting the different polymer varieties is expensive. On the other hand, polymers are durable and so take up landfill space, are visually polluting and in the seas can cause seabirds and other aquatic creatures to die from choking if they swallow plastic waste.

**Examiner tip**
The repeat unit of a polymer made by addition will contain a chain of two carbon atoms. Thus the repeat unit of (poly) propene is *not* $-(CH_2-CH_2-CH_2)-$.

**Knowledge check 38**
Write the repeat unit from the polymerisation of propenoic acid, $CH_2=CHCOOH$.

**Examiner tip**
Do not think that recycling plastics is carbon neutral, nor that using paper from trees instead of plastics is always better for the environment.

Given information on a particular product, you should weigh up the advantages and disadvantages of using it. You should recognise that there are no cost-free solutions to any of our efforts to make processes more sustainable.

**Summary**

After studying this topic, you should:

- be able to give the systematic names of alkanes and alkenes and of the products of their reactions
- be able to differentiate between hazard and risk
- be able to draw and name structural and *E/Z* (geometric) isomers of alkanes and alkenes
- know the equations and conditions for the reactions of:
  - alkanes with air (oxygen) and chlorine
  - alkenes with hydrogen, halogens, hydrogen halides and potassium manganate(VII)
- be able to deduce the repeat units of polymers given the formula of the monomer
- draw the mechanism of the free radical substitution reaction of alkanes
- draw the mechanism of electrophilic addition reactions of alkenes

# Questions & Answers

This section contains multiple-choice and structured questions similar to those you can expect to find in Unit Test 1. The questions given here are not balanced in terms of types of question or level of demand — that is, they are not intended to typify real papers, only the sorts of questions that could be asked.

In the examinations, the answers are written on the question paper. Here, the questions are not shown in examination paper format.

The answers given are those that examiners would expect from a grade-A candidate. They are not 'model answers' to be regurgitated without understanding. In answers that require more extended writing, it is usually the ideas that count rather than the form of words used; the principle is that correct and relevant chemistry scores.

## Examiner's comments

Responses to questions may have an examiner's comment, preceded by the icon ⊖. The comments may explain the correct answer, point out common errors made by candidates who produce work of C-grade or lower, or contain additional material that could be useful to you.

## The unit test

The unit test lasts 1 hour 30 minutes and is worth 80 marks. This unit counts for 40% of AS or 20% of A2 marks. Section A contains objective test (multiple-choice) questions; Section B contains a mixture of short-answer and extended-answer questions, including questions on the analysis and evaluation of practical work. Quality of written communication is assessed in Section B.

### Assessment objectives

Unit Test 1 has three assessment objectives (AOs).

AO1 is 'knowledge and understanding of science and of How Science Works'. This makes up 50% of Unit Test 1. You should be able to:
- recognise, recall and show understanding of scientific knowledge
- select, organise and present information clearly and logically, using specialist vocabulary where appropriate

AO2 is 'application of knowledge and understanding of science and of How Science Works'. This makes up 40% of Unit Test 1. You should be able to:
- analyse and evaluate scientific knowledge and processes
- apply scientific knowledge and processes to unfamiliar situations
- assess the validity, reliability and credibility of scientific information

AO3 is 'How Science Works'. This makes up 10% of Unit Test 1. You should be able to:

- demonstrate and describe ethical, safe and skilful practical techniqes and processes, selecting appropriate qualitative and quantitative methods
- make, record and communicate reliable and valid observations and measurements with appropriate precision and accuracy
- analyse, interpret, explain and evaluate the methodology, results and impact of your own and others' experimental and investigative activities in a variety of ways

## Command terms

The following command terms are used in the specification and in unit test questions. You must distinguish between them carefully.

- **Recall** — a simple remembering of facts learned, without any explanation or justification of these facts.
- **Understand** — be able to explain the relationship between facts and underlying chemical principles (understanding enables you to use facts in new situations).
- **Predict** — say what you think will happen on the basis of learned principles.
- **Define** — give a simple definition, without any explanation.
- **Determine** — find out.
- **Show** — relate one set of facts to another set.
- **Interpret** — take data or other types of information and use them to construct chemical theories or principles.
- **Describe** — state the characteristics of a particular material or thing.
- **Explain** — use chemical theories or principles to say why a particular property of a substance or series of substances is as it is.

# Approaching the unit test

The unit test is designed to allow you to show the examiner what you know. Answering questions successfully is not only a matter of knowing the chemistry, but is also a matter of technique. Unit Test 1 is a paper with multiple-choice, short-answer and extended-answer questions that are answered on the question paper.

## Revision

Start your revision in plenty of time. Make a list of the things that you need to do, emphasising the things that you find most difficult, and draw up a detailed revision plan. Work back from the examination date, ideally leaving an entire week free from fresh revision before that date. Be realistic in your revision plan and then add 25% to the timings because everything takes longer than you think.

When revising:

- make a note of difficulties and ask your teacher about them — if you do not make such notes, you will forget to ask
- make use of past papers, but remember that these have been written to a different specification
- revise ideas, rather than forms of words — you are after *understanding*
- remember that scholarship requires time to be spent on the work

When you use the example questions in this book, make a determined effort to answer them before looking up the answers and comments. Remember that the answers given here are not intended as model answers to be learnt parrot-fashion. They are answers designed to illuminate chemical ideas and understanding.

# The exam

## The exam paper

- Read the question. Questions usually change from one examination to the next. A question that looks the same, at a cursory glance, as one that you have seen before usually has significant differences when read carefully. Needless to say, candidates do not receive credit for writing answers to their own questions.
- Be aware of the number of marks available for a question. That is an excellent pointer to the number of things you need to say.
- Do not repeat the question in your answer. The danger is that you fill up the space available and think that you have answered the question, when in reality some or maybe all of the real points have been ignored.
- The name of a 'rule' is not an explanation for a chemical phenomenon. For example, in equilibrium (Unit 2), a common answer to a question on the effect of changing pressure on an equilibrium system is 'Because of le Chatelier's principle...'. That is simply a name for a rule — it does not explain anything.

## Multiple-choice questions

Answers to multiple-choice questions are machine-marked. Multiple-choice questions need to be read carefully; it is important not to jump to a conclusion about the answer too quickly. You need to be aware that one of the options might be a 'distracter'. An example of this might be in a question having a numerical answer of, say, $-600\,\text{kJ}\,\text{mol}^{-1}$; a likely distracter would be $+600\,\text{kJ}\,\text{mol}^{-1}$.

Some questions require you to think on paper — there is no demand that multiple-choice questions be carried out in your head. Space is provided on the question paper for rough working. It will not be marked, so do not write anything that matters in this space because no-one will see it.

For each of the questions there are four suggested answers, A, B, C and D. You select the best answer by putting a cross in the box beside the letter of your choice. If you change your mind you should put a line through the box and then indicate your alternative choice. Making more than one choice does not earn any marks. Note that this format is not used in the multiple-choice questions in this book.

The Unit 1 test has 20 multiple-choice questions, which should take you no more than 30 minutes.

# Marking

## Online marking

It is important that you have some understanding of how examinations are marked, because to some extent it affects how you answer them. Your examination technique partly concerns chemistry and partly must be geared to how the examinations are dealt with physically. You have to pay attention to the layout of what you write. Because all your scripts are scanned and marked online, there are certain things you must do to ensure that all your work is seen and marked. This is covered below.

As the examiner reads your answer, decisions have to be made — is this answer worth the mark or not? Your job is to give the *clearest possible answer* to the question asked, in such a way that your chemical understanding is made obvious to the examiner. In particular, you must not expect the examiner to guess what is in your head; you can be judged only by what you write.

Because examination answers cannot be discussed, you must make your answers as clear as possible. This is one reason why you are expected, for example, to show working in calculations. It is especially important that you *think before you write*. You will have a space for your answer on the question paper, and that space is what the examiner has judged to be a reasonable amount of space for the answer. Because of differing handwriting sizes, because of false starts and crossings-out, and because some candidates have a tendency to repeat the question in the answer space, that space is never exactly right for all candidates.

Edexcel exam scripts are marked online, so few examiners will handle a real, original script. The process is as follows:

- When the paper is set it is divided up into items, often, but not necessarily, a single part of a question. These items are also called clips.
- The items are set up so that they display on-screen, with check-boxes for the score and various buttons to allow the score to be submitted or for the item to be processed in some other way.
- After you have written your paper it is scanned; from that point all the handling of your paper is electronic. Your answers are tagged with an identity number.
- It is impossible for an examiner to identify a centre or a candidate from any of the information supplied.

## Common pitfalls

The following list of potential pitfalls to avoid is particularly important:

- **Do *not* write in any colour other than black.** This is now an exam board regulation. The scans are entirely black-and-white, so any colour used simply comes out black — unless you write in red, in which case it does not come out at all. The scanner cannot see red (or pink or orange) writing. So if, for example, you want to highlight different areas under a graph, or distinguish lines on a graph, you must use a different sort of shading rather than a different colour.
- **Do *not* use small writing.** Because the answer appears on a screen, the definition is slightly degraded. In particular, small numbers used for powers of 10 can be difficult to see. The original script is always available but it takes a relatively long time to get hold of it.
- **Do *not* write in pencil.** Faint writing does not scan well.
- **Do *not* write outside the space provided without saying, within that space, where the remainder of the answer can be found.** Examiners only have access to a given item; they cannot see any other part of your script. So if you carry on your answer elsewhere but do not tell the examiner within the clip that it exists, it will not be seen. Although the examiner cannot mark the out-of-clip work, the paper will be referred to the Principal Examiner responsible for the paper.

- **Do *not* use asterisks or arrows as a means of directing examiners where to look for out-of-clip items.** Tell them in words. Candidates use asterisks for all sorts of things and examiners cannot be expected to guess what they mean.
- **Do *not* write across the centre-fold of the paper from the left-hand to the right-hand page.** A strip about 8 mm wide is lost when the papers are guillotined for scanning.
- **Do *not* repeat the question in your answer.** If you have a questions such as 'Define the first ionisation energy of calcium', the answer is 'The energy change per mole for the formation of unipositive ions from isolated calcium atoms in the gas phase'; or, using the equation, 'The energy change per mole for $Ca(g) \rightarrow Ca^+(g) + e^-$'. Do not start by writing 'The first ionisation energy for calcium is defined as...' because by then you will have taken up most of the space available for the answer. Examiners know what the question is — they can see it on the paper.

# Multiple-choice questions

See page 59 for details of how this type of question will appear on the papers.

Each of the questions or incomplete statements is followed by four suggested answers, A, B, C or D. Select the *best* answer in each case. The answers are given, with some commentary, after question 10.

1  The definition of the mole is:

A  the number of atoms in exactly 12 grams of the isotope $^{12}_{6}C$

B  the number of molecules in $24\,dm^3$ of a gas at 273 K and 1 atm

C  the number of molecules in $24\,dm^3$ of a gas at room temperature and 1 atm

D  the amount of any substance containing the same number of elementary entities as there are atoms in exactly 12 grams of the isotope $^{12}_{6}C$

2  Which one of the following equations is associated with the definition of the standard enthalpy of formation of carbon monoxide?

A  $C(s) + \frac{1}{2}O_2(g) \rightarrow CO(g)$    B  $C(graphite) + \frac{1}{2}O_2(g) \rightarrow CO(g)$

C  $C(s) + O(g) \rightarrow CO(g)$    D  $C(g) + \frac{1}{2}O_2(g) \rightarrow CO(g)$

3  If the average C–H bond enthalpy is +x, which one of the following represents a process with enthalpy change +4x?

A  $C(g) + 4H(g) \rightarrow CH_4(g)$    B  $CH_4(g) \rightarrow C(g) + 4H(g)$

C  $CH_4(g) \rightarrow C(g) + 2H_2(g)$    D  $C(s) + 2H_2(g) \rightarrow CH_4(g)$

4  The elements of group 1 (Li–Cs) are very electropositive because:

A  they all have small atomic radii

B  their ions all have low hydration enthalpies

C  they all have low first ionisation energies

D  they all have high second ionisation energies

5  The structure of butan-2-ol is represented by the skeletal formula:

6  Which of the processes A–D is a propagation step in the reaction between chlorine and methane in the presence of ultraviolet light?

A  $\cdot CH_3 + Cl\cdot \rightarrow CH_3Cl$    B  $CH_4 + Cl\cdot \rightarrow CH_3Cl + H\cdot$

C  $CH_4 + Cl_2 \rightarrow CH_3Cl + HCl$    D  $CH_4 + Cl\cdot \rightarrow \cdot CH_3 + HCl$

7  Ethoxyethane, usually known as ether, is often used to extract organic compounds from aqueous solution. Which of its properties A–D does *not* favour its selection for this use?

A  it dissolves most organic compounds easily    B  it is immiscible with water

C  its air/vapour mixture is explosive    D  it is inert to most types of reaction

8   In an experiment to measure the enthalpy of neutralisation of hydrochloric acid, 25.0 cm³ of hydrochloric acid containing 0.050 mol of HCl was reacted with 25.0 cm³ of sodium hydroxide solution of the same concentration in an expanded polystyrene cup. The temperature rise was 13.7°C. The heat capacity of the solution is $4.2 J g^{-1}°C^{-1}$ and the density is $1.00 g cm^{-3}$. What is the enthalpy of neutralisation of hydrochloric acid (to 3 s.f.)?

   **A** $-57.5 kJ mol^{-1}$                          **B** $+57.5 kJ mol^{-1}$

   **C** $-28.8 kJ mol^{-1}$                          **D** $-2.88 kJ mol^{-1}$

9   The use of large amounts of disposable poly(alkene) packaging has been criticised because:

   **A** a large amount of fossil fuel is burnt during its manufacture

   **B** the combustion of poly(alkenes) produces dangerous fumes

   **C** poly(alkenes) degrade to produce toxic materials

   **D** a large amount of fossil fuel is converted to the necessary monomers, such as ethene

10  The set of ions in which the members all have the same electron configuration is:

   **A** $Fe^{2+}$, $Fe^{3+}$                          **B** $N^{3-}$, $O^{2-}$, $F^-$

   **C** $SO_4^{2-}$, $SeO_4^{2-}$, $TeO_4^{2-}$       **D** $F^-$, $Cl^-$, $Br^-$

## Student answer

**1** D

ℯ The general definition of the mole has to be able to cope with particles other than atoms. Therefore the definition is **D**, with the proviso that 'the elementary entities must be specified and may be atoms, molecules, ions, electrons, other particles, or specified groups of such particles' (International Committee for Weights and Measures, 1971 and 1980). Option **A** is a statement related to the value of the Avogadro constant.

**2** B

ℯ This answer makes clear that the most stable form of the element carbon under standard conditions is graphite. This makes option **B** of higher quality than **A**, which is nearly right. Hence the exhortation in the introduction to read the questions carefully and not to make up your mind too soon.

**3** B

ℯ The bond enthalpy relates to the energy change in the production of atoms, so isolated atoms must be the product if all four of the bonds in methane are broken.

**4** C

ℯ The low ionisation energies mean that this endothermic change can be recovered from the bonding produced when the cation and the anion attract one another. Options **A** and **B** are both the opposite of the truth, but **D** is true. Some of the incorrect answers to the question set can be statements which in themselves are true. This is a common source of error in multiple-choice papers.

**5  C**

**e** The chain contains four carbon atoms with the –OH group on the second carbon. Formula A is butan-1-ol, and B and D are isomers of the 5-carbon alcohol, pentanol.

**6  D**

**e** The propagation steps must produce a radical for every radical that is used, so, on this basis alone, **B** could be an answer. However, answers do have to correspond with what actually happens in the universe.

**7  C**

**e** This is a *hazard* that must be overcome if ether is to be used. The *risk* from its explosive nature depends on how the ether is used. Using a fume cupboard and ensuring that there are no naked flames are obvious solutions. Perhaps there are other less hazardous solvents that, in a given circumstance, could be used instead.

**8  A**

**e** The calculation is:

$$\Delta H = \frac{-50.0\,g \times 4.2\,Jg^{-1}{}^{\circ}C^{-1} \times 13.7{}^{\circ}C}{0.050\,mol}$$

$$= -57.540\,Jmol^{-1} \text{ or } -57.5\,kJmol^{-1} \text{ to the required 3 s.f.}$$

The other values are distracters arising from common errors in this type of calculation. The value is negative because the temperature has risen and so the reaction must be exothermic.

**9  D**

**e** None of answers A–C is true.

**10  B**

**e** All of these ions have the electron configuration $1s^2\,2s^2\,2p^6$, i.e. that of neon.

# Structured questions

# Question 11

Crude oil contains a large proportion of alkanes, which form a homologous series.

(a) (i)  Explain the meaning of the term 'homologous series', using the alkanes as your example.   (2 marks)

ⓔ Note that the question requires a reference to the homologous series of alkanes.

(ii)  Alkanes exhibit structural isomerism. Draw the displayed formulae of the three structural isomers of the alkane $C_5H_{12}$.   (3 marks)

ⓔ Make sure that you write in all the hydrogen atoms. Using 'sticks' will not score full marks.

(b) Methane reacts with chlorine in the presence of UV light to give chloromethane and hydrogen chloride:

$$CH_4 + Cl_2 \rightarrow CH_3Cl + HCl$$

(i)  What type of reaction is this?   (1 mark)
(ii)  The first step of the mechanism involves homolytic fission. Explain the meaning of this term.   (1 mark)
(iii) Give the mechanism for the reaction between methane and chlorine, making clear which are the initiation, propagation and termination steps.   (6 marks)

ⓔ The initiation step should be shown using the correct type of curly arrow. The other steps do not require curly arrows, but radicals must be shown with a •.

Total: 13 marks

### Student answer

(a) (i)  A series of compounds with the same general formula, in this case $C_nH_{2n+2}$ ✓, and showing similar chemical properties ✓.

ⓔ The inclusion of the particular general formula is necessary to make the answer refer to the alkanes, as required by the question. If asked about a specific type of compound, make sure that your answer is specific, not general.

(a) (ii)

(b) (i)  (Free) radical substitution ✓

**(b) (ii)** Breaking a covalent bond so that one electron goes to each of the two species formed, which are radicals ✓

**(b) (iii)** Initiation: $Cl\!-\!Cl \longrightarrow 2Cl\bullet$ ✓

Propagation:

$$CH_4 + Cl\bullet \rightarrow \bullet CH_3 + HCl ✓$$
$$\bullet CH_3 + Cl_2 \rightarrow CH_3Cl + Cl\bullet ✓$$

Termination:

$$2Cl\bullet \rightarrow Cl_2 ✓$$
$$Cl\bullet + \bullet CH_3 \rightarrow CH_3Cl ✓$$
$$2 \bullet CH_3 \rightarrow C_2H_6 ✓$$

ⓔ A common error is to have an impossible propagation step such as $CH_4 + Cl\bullet \rightarrow CH_3Cl + H\bullet$. Not only are the bond energies unfavourable, but also the mechanism is the removal of an H radical by a Cl radical.

# Question 12

**(a) State Hess's law.** (2 marks)

**(b) Define the term 'standard enthalpy of combustion'.** (3 marks)

ⓔ Do not forget to state what is meant by 'standard conditions'.

**(c) The equation for the combustion of ethanol in air is:**

$$C_2H_5OH(l) + 3O_2(g) \rightarrow 2CO_2(g) + 3H_2O(l)$$

**Calculate the enthalpy change for this reaction using the average bond enthalpy values given in the table.** (3 marks)

| Bond | Average bond enthalpy/kJ mol$^{-1}$ | Bond | Average bond enthalpy/kJ mol$^{-1}$ |
|------|------|------|------|
| C–H | +412 | C–C | +348 |
| C–O | +360 | O–H | +463 |
| O=O | +496 | C=O | +743 |

ⓔ Make sure that you give a sign and units with your answer.

**Total: 8 marks**

**Student answer**

**(a)** The heat energy/enthalpy change in a chemical reaction is independent of the route used to go from the reagents to the products ✓ provided that the initial and final states are the same ✓.

ⓔ The term 'energy change' alone should not be used — this refers to a reaction at constant volume, not constant pressure.

> **(b)** The heat energy change per mole ✓ for the complete combustion of a substance in excess oxygen ✓ at 1 atm pressure and stated temperature ✓.

ⓔ In practice, quoting the temperature as 298 K would also gain credit, although this particular temperature is not part of the definition of the standard state. *Heat* energy change, not energy change alone, is important. The energy change for a reaction is given the symbol $\Delta U$ and is measured at constant volume, not constant pressure.

> **(c)** There is no standard notation for the average bond enthalpy. Using $D(X–X)$ to refer to it for the X–X bond:
>
> $\Delta H$ = (sum of bond energies of reagents) – (sum of bond energies of the products) ✓
>
> $= [5D(C–H) + D(C–O) + D(C–C) + D(O–H) + 3D(O=O)] – [4D(C=O) + 6D(O–H)]$ ✓
>
> $= [(5 \times 412) + 360 + 348 + 463 + (3 \times 496)] – [(4 \times 743) + (6 \times 463)] = -1031\,\text{kJ}\,\text{mol}^{-1}$ ✓

ⓔ Note that brackets are used to separate the enthalpy values for each type of bond. The absence of such working is characteristic of C-grade answers and is a high-risk strategy. If the answer only is shown and it is wrong, you cannot get marks for intermediate steps.

Remember that bond making is exothermic and bond breaking endothermic.

Be careful to choose the correct values — it is common to find, for example, that the C–O bond strength is used for the C=O bond.

# Question 13

> **(a) (i)** Complete the electron configuration of a sulfur atom: $1s^2$....      (1 mark)
>      **(ii)** State the number of neutrons in the nucleus of an atom of $^{32}$S.      (1 mark)
> **(b) (i)** Define the term 'first electron affinity'.      (2 marks)

ⓔ Make sure that you say what physical states the species are in or include state symbols in an equation.

>      **(ii)** The following equation represents the change occurring when the second electron affinity of sulfur is measured:
>
>         $S^-(g) + e^- \rightarrow S^{2-}(g)$
>
>      Explain why the second electron affinity of an element is always endothermic.      (2 marks)

**Total: 6 marks**

**Student answer**

**(a) (i)**   $1s^2\,2s^2\,2p^6\,3s^2\,3p^4$ ✓

**(a) (ii)**   $32 - 16 = 16$ ✓

ⓔ This question requires you to use the periodic table that is provided with all question papers. It is, of course, another way of finding out if you know what the terms atomic number and mass number mean.

**(b) (i)** The energy change for the addition of one electron to each atom in one mole of atoms ✓ in the gas phase ✓.

ⓔ This could be answered by means of one statement with an equation, namely: the energy change per mole ✓ for the process:

$$X(g) + e^- \rightarrow X^-(g) \checkmark$$

**(b) (ii)** The negative electron is being added to a negative ion ✓ and the two negative charges repel ✓.

ⓔ Succeeding electron affinities would also be positive (endothermic); in practice, simple ions of charge greater than 3− are not seen.

# Question 14

**(a)** When a sample of copper is analysed using a mass spectrometer, its atoms are ionised, accelerated, and then separated according to their mass/charge (*m/e*) ratio.
  **(i)** Explain how the atoms of the sample are ionised. (2 marks)
  **(ii)** State how the resulting ions are accelerated. (1 mark)
  **(iii)** State how the ions are separated according to their *m/e* values. (1 mark)

**(b)** For a particular sample of copper, two peaks were obtained in the mass spectrum, showing an abundance of 69.10% at *m/e* 63, and 30.90% at *m/e* 65.
  **(i)** Give the formula of the species responsible for the peak at *m/e* 65. (1 mark)

ⓔ A perfect answer would include the atomic number, the mass number and any charge on the species.

  **(ii)** State why two peaks, at *m/e* values of 63 and 65, were obtained in the mass spectrum, but no peak is found at an *m/e* value of 64. (2 marks)
  **(iii)** Calculate the relative atomic mass of this sample of copper to three significant figures, using the data given above. (2 marks)

**Total: 9 marks**

Student answer

**(a) (i)** Fast-moving *or* energetic electrons strike the atoms ✓ removing electrons from the sample atoms, forming positive ions ✓.

ⓔ The copper sample would be on a heated probe; although the vapour pressure of copper is very small, the number of atoms volatilised at the extremely low pressure in the mass spectrometer is large enough to be detected.

Edexcel AS Chemistry

**(a) (ii)** In an electric *or* electrostatic field ✓

**(a) (iii)** By a magnetic field ✓

**(b) (i)** $^{65}Cu^+$ ✓

ⓔ Many candidates forget to put the essential positive charge when giving the formulae of the ions detected by a mass spectrometer.

**(b) (ii)** Because naturally-occurring copper contains two isotopes of mass 63 and 65 ✓. There are no $Cu_2$ molecules, so there is no peak at m/e = 64 ✓.

**(b) (iii)** Relative atomic mass $= \dfrac{(63 \times 69.10) + (65 \times 30.90)}{(69.10 + 30.90)}$ ✓ $= 63.6$ ✓

ⓔ The question asks for *three* significant figures. If you give 63.618 or 63.62 you will not score the mark. This is a silly way to lose marks.

# Question 15

**(a) Explain the following observations. Include details of the *bonding* in, and the *structure* of, each substance.**

**(i) The melting temperature of diamond is much higher than that of iodine.** (5 marks)

ⓔ You must state the type of structures of both iodine and diamond, the type of forces between the particles and the relationship between the strength and the melting temperature.

**(ii) Sodium chloride has a high melting temperature (approximately 800°C)** (3 marks)

ⓔ As above, the type of structure and force must be described.

**(b) Explain in terms of its structure and bonding why aluminium is a good conductor of electricity.** (3 marks)

ⓔ Read the question carefully. You must first answer about the structure and bonding of aluminium and then explain why this allows it to conduct electricity.

**Total: 11 marks**

| Student answer |

**(a) (i)** Iodine is molecular covalent ✓ so has weak intermolecular forces ✓; diamond is giant covalent ✓, so has strong intramolecular covalent bonds throughout the crystal lattice ✓. The stronger the forces, the more energy is needed to overcome them to melt the crystal ✓.

ⓔ When discussing the bonding of covalent substances, it is important to distinguish between *inter*molecular forces, which exist between *molecules*, and *intra*molecular forces, which are between *atoms*. Covalent bonds are strong.

**(a) (ii)** Sodium chloride has a lattice ✓ of oppositely charged ions ✓ with strong attractions throughout the lattice ✓.

ⓔ The extension of the attractions throughout the lattice is important. There are no pairs of ions that can be selected over any other pair; the attraction is uniform throughout the crystal. There are also repulsions in the lattice between ions of the same charge; the attraction is a net attraction.

**(b)** Metal ions are in a lattice ✓ bonded by attraction to delocalised electrons *or* embedded in a sea of electrons ✓. Mobile electrons enable conduction ✓.

ⓔ Make sure that you say that the electrons are mobile. Just saying that they form a 'sea' is not enough. It is also important to say that the electrons are attracted to the ions.

# Question 16

**(a) Lithium chloride, LiCl, can be made by the reaction of lithium with chlorine:**

$$2Li(s) + Cl_2(g) \rightarrow 2LiCl(s)$$

**(i) Calculate the maximum mass of lithium chloride that can be made from 35 g of lithium.** (2 marks)

ⓔ The route is mass of lithium → moles of lithium → moles of lithium chloride → mass of lithium chloride.

**(ii) Calculate the concentration in $mol\,dm^{-3}$ of the solution that would be obtained if this mass of lithium chloride were dissolved in water to make $5.00\,dm^3$ of solution.** (1 mark)

**(iii) Calculate the volume of chlorine gas required to react with 35 g of lithium. The molar volume of a gas at the temperature and pressure of the experiment is $24\,dm^3$.** (2 marks)

ⓔ The route is moles of lithium → moles of chlorine → volume of chlorine.

**(b) Explain why lithium has a higher melting temperature than sodium.** (3 marks)

ⓔ You must understand metallic bonding to be able to answer this question. What are the forces involved and why are they stronger in one metal than in the other?

**(c) (i) Define the term 'first ionisation energy'.** (3 marks)

ⓔ You must state the amounts and the physical states (or state symbols if an equation is used) of all species.

**(ii) Explain why the first ionisation energy of lithium is less endothermic than the first ionisation energy of neon.** (3 marks)

**(iii) Explain why the first ionisation energy of sodium is less endothermic than that of lithium.** (3 marks)

ⓔ You must compare the nuclear charges, the amounts of screening and the sizes of each.

**Total: 17 marks**

**Student answer**

**(a) (i)** moles of lithium used = 35 g ÷ 7.0 g mol$^{-1}$ = 5.0 mol ✓ = moles of LiCl

mass of LiCl produced = 5.0 mol × 42.5 g mol$^{-1}$ = 212.5 g ✓

**(a) (ii)** concentration = 5.0 mol ÷ 5.00 dm$^3$ = 1.0 mol dm$^{-3}$ ✓

**(a) (iii)** 1 mol Li reacts with 0.5 mol $Cl_2$ ✓

∴ volume $Cl_2$ required = 0.5 × 5.0 mol × 24 dm$^3$ mol$^{-1}$ = 60 dm$^3$ ✓

ⓔ Note that the use of units throughout the calculations enables you to check that what you are doing is correct, since the units of the answer will also be correct.

**(b)** The lithium ion ✓ is smaller ✓ than the sodium ion, so the attraction between it and the delocalised electrons is greater ✓, making it harder to melt.

ⓔ Make sure that your answer refers to *both* sodium and lithium. Use of the word 'atom' for ion would lose 1 mark.

**(c) (i)** The energy change ✓ for the formation of a mole of gaseous unipositive ions ✓ from a mole of gaseous atoms ✓.

*or*

The energy change per mole ✓ for the process:

E(g) → E$^+$(g) + e$^-$ ✓✓

ⓔ If you can define things through equations, do so. It is often quicker and clearer. The equation scores 2 marks because it includes both the positive ion and the gas phase.

Note that for chlorine it is the energy change for Cl(g) → Cl$^+$(g) + e$^-$ and *not* for ½Cl$_2$(g) → Cl$^+$(g) + e$^-$

**(c) (ii)** The lithium atom is larger than the neon atom ✓ and the nuclear charge of lithium is lower than that of neon ✓. Both have two inner/shielding electrons, so the single outer electron is more effectively shielded from the +3 nucleus by the two inner electrons in lithium, whereas the outer eight electrons in neon are less shielded from the +10 nucleus by the two inner electrons.

**(c) (iii)** Sodium is a larger atom than lithium ✓. The greater nuclear charge in sodium is offset ✓ by the increased number of shells, so there are increased repulsions/more shielding from the inner electrons ✓.

ⓔ The idea of repulsion from inner electrons is sometimes expressed as shielding of the nuclear charge from the outer electrons by the inner ones. Some students find the notion of repulsions easier to visualise.

# Question 17

**(a) State Hess's law.** $\qquad$ (2 marks)

**(b) Methane burns in oxygen:**

$$CH_4(g) + 2O_2(g) \rightarrow CO_2(g) + 2H_2O(g)$$

(i) **Use your *Data Booklet* to find appropriate values of the bond enthalpies needed to calculate the enthalpy change for this reaction.**
(2 marks)

ⓔ Do not use average values of bond enthalpies if the ones for the actual molecule are given in the data booklet.

(ii) **Calculate this enthalpy change.**
(3 marks)

ⓔ Do not forget to include a sign and units with your answer.

(iii) **If the enthalpy change for the reaction is calculated using *standard* enthalpies of formation, its value is $-890\,kJ\,mol^{-1}$. What is meant by the term 'standard'?**
(2 marks)
(iv) **Explain why the value given in (iii) is different from that obtained in (ii).**
(2 marks)

ⓔ Consider what values you used in (b) (i) and what the term standard means in (b) (iii).

**Total: 11 marks**

### Student answer

**(a)** The enthalpy change for a reaction is independent of the path taken ✓ provided that the initial and final states are the same ✓.

**(b) (i)** Bond enthalpies/$kJ\,mol^{-1}$: C–H 435, O=O 498, C=O 805, O–H 464.

ⓔ The *Data Booklet* is a feature of Edexcel examinations and the ability to use it correctly is essential. In this question, the bond enthalpy values for the particular molecules involved are needed, so the ability to select these values, rather than average ones, is important.

**(b) (ii)** bonds broken = 4(C–H) + 2(O=O)

so, energy used = $(4 \times 435) + (2 \times 498) = 2736\,kJ\,mol^{-1}$ ✓

bonds made = 2(C=O) + 4(O–H)

so, energy gained = $(2 \times 805) + (4 \times 464) = 3466\,kJ\,mol^{-1}$ ✓

$\Delta H = 2736 - 3466\,kJ\,mol^{-1} = -730\,kJ\,mol^{-1}$ ✓

ⓔ In every calculation that you do, you must include the units. It doesn't matter whether there are marks available or not; you are dealing with physical quantities, and physical quantities have units. The aim is to understand chemistry — a separate idea from merely gaining marks in an examination.

**(b) (iii)** The standard state refers to all substances being at 1 atm pressure ✓ and a stated temperature ✓, usually 298 K.

ⓔ If no other temperature is stated, 298 K is taken as the temperature.

# Structured questions

**(b) (iv)** The bond enthalpy calculation in (b) (ii) is made on the basis that gaseous water is formed ✓. The one using *standard* enthalpies of formation has liquid water as the product. The change from gaseous to liquid water gives out heat ✓ so the two values are significantly different.

ⓔ Avoid the knee-jerk reaction 'because average bond enthalpies were used' as the ones used in (b) (i) were specific to the molecules in the question.

# Question 18

**(a) Methane reacts with chlorine in the presence of ultraviolet light.**
  **(i)**  **Give the equation for the reaction that produces chloromethane.**    (1 mark)
  **(ii)** **Explain why some dichloromethane, $CH_2Cl_2$, and some ethane, $C_2H_6$, are also produced when this reaction takes place.**    (4 marks)

ⓔ To answer this you must understand the mechanism. With which species, that will be present during the course of the reaction, could a chlorine radical or a methyl radical collide?

**(b) Alkenes react with bromine, but light is not needed.**
  **(i)**  **Give the equation for the reaction with ethene and state what you would see.**    (2 marks)
  **(ii)** **Give the mechanism for the reaction of an alkene with bromine.**    (3 marks)

**Total: 10 marks**

## Student answer

**(a) (i)**  $CH_4 + Cl_2 \rightarrow CH_3Cl + HCl$ ✓

**(a) (ii)**  A chlorine radical could collide with a $CH_3Cl$ molecule produced earlier ✓. This will form some $CH_2Cl_2$ by the propagation steps:

    $CH_3Cl + Cl\bullet \rightarrow \bullet CH_2Cl + HCl$ ✓

    Then $\bullet CH_2Cl + Cl_2 \rightarrow CH_2Cl_2 + Cl\bullet$ ✓

    Ethane is formed in the chain-breaking step:

    $CH_3\bullet + CH_3\bullet \rightarrow C_2H_6$ ✓

ⓔ The reaction is not instantaneous, so some chlorine radicals will collide with $CH_3Cl$ molecules produced earlier rather than with unreacted $CH_4$ molecules.

**(b) (i)**  $H_2C=CH_2 + Br_2 \rightarrow BrCH_2CH_2Br$ ✓
    The brown colour of bromine is lost ✓.

ⓔ Do *not* say that the bromine goes clear. Bromine is a clear brown colour.
    If bromine water is used, the product is $CH_2BrCH_2OH$, caused by the addition of HOBr, which is formed by the reaction $Br_2 + H_2O \rightarrow HOBr + HBr$.

**(b) (ii)**

There is 1 mark for the first two arrows, 1 mark for the intermediate carbocation and 1 mark for the attack of the bromide ion on the carbocation. Note that curly arrows show the movement of electron pairs, so they must start and finish in the proper places. A curly arrow must start from a bond or from an atom or ion. It must go to an atom to form an ion or *towards* an atom to form a bond. Lone pairs should be shown but their omission will not be penalised.

## Knowledge check answers

**1** Number of methane molecules $= 0.125\,\text{mol} \times 6.02 \times 10^{23}\,\text{mol}^{-1}$
$= 7.53 \times 10^{22}$

**2** Total number of ions $= 5 \times 0.125\,\text{mol} \times 6.02 \times 10^{23}\,\text{mol}^{-1}$
$= 3.76 \times 10^{23}$

**3** (a) $12.0 + 4.0 = 16\,\text{g}$
(b) $23.0 + 35.5 = 58.5\,\text{g}$

**4** (a) moles = mass/molar mass $= 2.0\,\text{g}/16.0\,\text{g mol}^{-1} = 0.125\,\text{mol}$
(b) moles $= 2.0\,\text{g}/58.5\,\text{g mol}^{-1} = 0.034\,\text{mol}$

**5** mass = moles × molar mass $= 0.12\,\text{mol} \times 40\,\text{g mol}^{-1} = 4.8\,\text{g}$

**6** Volume of solution $= 250/1000\,\text{dm}^3$
Moles of NaOH needed = concentration × volume in $\text{dm}^3$
$= 0.100\,\text{mol dm}^{-3} \times 0.250\,\text{dm}^3$
$= 0.0250\,\text{mol}$
Mass of NaOH needed = moles × molar mass
$= 0.0250\,\text{mol} \times 40.0\,\text{g mol}^{-1} = 1.00\,\text{g}$

**7** $2Al + 6HCl \rightarrow 2AlCl_3 + 3H_2$

**8** $Sn^{2+} + 2Fe^{3+} \rightarrow Sn^{4+} + 2Fe^{2+}$

**9** Volume = moles × molar volume $= 0.0246\,\text{mol} \times 24\,\text{dm}^3\,\text{mol}^{-1}$
$= 0.59\,\text{dm}^3$

**10** The atom economy of the first reaction will be less than that of the second.
1st reaction: atom economy $= 88.0 \times 100.0/(78.5 + 46.0)$
$= 71\%$
2nd reaction: atom economy $= 88.0 \times 100.0/(60.0 + 46.0) = 83\%$

**11** $\Delta H = 2 \times 111.9 = 223.8\,\text{kJ mol}^{-1}$

**12** Error $= 2 \times 0.5 = 1^{\circ}\text{C}$
$\Delta\theta = 26.0 - 18.5 = 7.5^{\circ}\text{C}$
% error $= 1 \times 100/7.5 = 13\%$

**13** Heat change $= mc\Delta\theta = 100\,\text{g} \times 4.2\,\text{J K}^{-1}\,\text{g}^{-1} \times 15\,\text{K} = 6300\,\text{J}$
Amount of ethanol = mass/molar mass $= 0.23\,\text{g}/46.0\,\text{g mol}^{-1}$
$= 0.0050\,\text{mol}$
$\Delta H = -6300\,\text{J}/0.0050\,\text{mol} = -1\,260\,000\,\text{J mol}^{-1}$
$= -1260\,\text{kJ mol}^{-1}$

**14**

| Bonds broken | Value/ kJ mol$^{-1}$ | Bonds made | Value/ kJ mol$^{-1}$ |
|---|---|---|---|
| C=C | 612 | C–H | 413 |
| H–Cl | 432 | C–Cl | 346 |
| | | C–C | 347 |
| Total | 1044 | Total | 1106 |

$\Delta H_{\text{reaction}} = 1044 - 1106 = -62\,\text{kJ mol}^{-1}$
*Do not forget that a new C–C has to be made as the calculation assumed that the C=C was completely broken.*

**15** Equation 1: $CuSO_4.5H_2O(s) \rightarrow CuSO_4(aq)$ $\Delta H = +6\,\text{kJ mol}^{-1}$
Equation 2: $CuSO_4(s) \rightarrow CuSO_4(aq)$ $\Delta H = -73\,\text{kJ mol}^{-1}$
Reversing equation 2 and adding to equation 1 gives
$CuSO_4.5H_2O(s) \rightarrow CuSO_4(s)\ (+5H_2O(l))$
$\Delta H = +6 - (-73) = +79\,\text{kJ mol}^{-1}$

**16** It will have three peaks. One at $m/e = 158$ due to $(^{79}Br-^{79}Br)^+$, one at 160 due to $(^{79}Br-^{81}Br)^+$, and one at 162 due to $(^{81}Br-^{81}Br)^+$.

**17** (a) Si: $1s^2\ 2s^2\ 2p^6\ 3s^2\ 3p^2$
(b) Mn: $1s^2\ 2s^2\ 2p^6\ 3s^2\ 3p^6\ 4s^2\ 3d^5$

**18** (a) $\left[\begin{array}{c} \times\times \\ \times\ \text{Mg}\ \times \\ \times\times \end{array}\right]^{2+}$

(b) $\left[\begin{array}{c} \times\times \\ \times\times \\ \times \\ \times\times\ \text{Cl}\ \times\times \\ \times \\ \times\times \\ \times\times \end{array}\right]^{-}$

**19** There are strong electrostatic forces between the oppositely charged ions. A lot of energy is therefore needed to separate the ions.

**20** Both ions have 10 electrons but the $F^-$ ion has 9 protons whereas the $O^{2-}$ ion has 8. This means that there is less attraction in the $O^{2-}$ ion between the nucleus and the outer electrons.

**21** The $Na^+$ ion is smaller than the $K^+$ ion, so the distance between the positive and negative ions is less in NaCl than in KCl. The result (by Coulomb's law) is that the force of attraction is greater and more energy is released in forming the lattice.

**22** $NaCl < MgCl_2 < MgBr_2$

**23** The formation of $Na^{2+}$ ions would require an electron to be removed from the inner shell. This would be hugely endothermic and would not be compensated for by the slight extra lattice energy.

**24** 10 electrons

**25**

**26** There are weak intermolecular forces between *molecules* of oxygen but strong covalent bonds between *atoms* in diamond and graphite.

**27** :Cl ̈ ×̈ P ×̈ Cl: ̈
 :Cl: ̈

**28** Magnesium has more delocalised electrons and a smaller ionic radius than sodium, so the forces between the ions and the delocalised electrons is stronger.

**29** A secondary alcohol and an alkene

**30** 2,2'-dimethylbutane

**31** 3,4-dimethylhex-2-ene

**32** The ether is very flammable (all organic compounds are flammable (and as it is very volatile the hazard is considerable) so warm the boiling tube with a beaker of hot water rather than a Bunsen flame.

**33** First hazard: concentrated sulfuric acid is corrosive. Risk reduced by wearing gloves.
Second hazard: gaseous bromine is toxic and harmful when breathed. Risk reduced by carrying out the experiment in a fume cupboard.

**34**

**35** There are two hydrogen atoms on the left-hand carbon atom.

**36** The $CH_3$ on the second carbon atom and the $C_2H_5$ on the right have the higher priorities. They are on opposite sides of the double bond, so *E*.

**37**

**38**

Page numbers in **bold** refer to definitions.

# The periodic table

Group

**Key:**

| Relative atomic mass |
| **Atomic symbol** |
| name |
| Atomic (proton) number |

| Period | 1 | 2 | | | | | | | | | | | | | 3 | 4 | 5 | 6 | 7 | 0 |
|---|---|---|---|---|---|---|---|---|---|---|---|---|---|---|---|---|---|---|---|---|
| 1 | 1.0<br>H<br>hydrogen<br>1 | | | | | | | | | | | | | | | | | | | 4.0<br>He<br>helium<br>2 |
| 2 | 6.9<br>Li<br>lithium<br>3 | 9.0<br>Be<br>beryllium<br>4 | | | | | | | | | | | | | 10.8<br>B<br>boron<br>5 | 12.0<br>C<br>carbon<br>6 | 14.0<br>N<br>nitrogen<br>7 | 16.0<br>O<br>oxygen<br>8 | 19.0<br>F<br>fluorine<br>9 | 20.2<br>Ne<br>neon<br>10 |
| 3 | 23.0<br>Na<br>sodium<br>11 | 24.3<br>Mg<br>magnesium<br>12 | | | | | | | | | | | | | 27.0<br>Al<br>aluminium<br>13 | 28.1<br>Si<br>silicon<br>14 | 31.0<br>P<br>phosphorus<br>15 | 32.1<br>S<br>sulfur<br>16 | 35.5<br>Cl<br>chlorine<br>17 | 39.9<br>Ar<br>argon<br>18 |
| 4 | 39.1<br>K<br>potassium<br>19 | 40.1<br>Ca<br>calcium<br>20 | 45.0<br>Sc<br>scandium<br>21 | 47.9<br>Ti<br>titanium<br>22 | 50.9<br>V<br>vanadium<br>23 | 52.0<br>Cr<br>chromium<br>24 | 54.9<br>Mn<br>manganese<br>25 | 55.8<br>Fe<br>iron<br>26 | 58.9<br>Co<br>cobalt<br>27 | 58.7<br>Ni<br>nickel<br>28 | 63.5<br>Cu<br>copper<br>29 | 65.4<br>Zn<br>zinc<br>30 | | | 69.7<br>Ga<br>gallium<br>31 | 72.6<br>Ge<br>germanium<br>32 | 74.9<br>As<br>arsenic<br>33 | 79.0<br>Se<br>selenium<br>34 | 79.9<br>Br<br>bromine<br>35 | 83.8<br>Kr<br>krypton<br>36 |
| 5 | 85.5<br>Rb<br>rubidium<br>37 | 87.6<br>Sr<br>strontium<br>38 | 88.9<br>Y<br>yttrium<br>39 | 91.2<br>Zr<br>zirconium<br>40 | 92.9<br>Nb<br>niobium<br>41 | 95.9<br>Mo<br>molybdenum<br>42 | [98]<br>Tc<br>technetium<br>43 | 101.1<br>Ru<br>ruthenium<br>44 | 102.9<br>Rh<br>rhodium<br>45 | 106.4<br>Pd<br>palladium<br>46 | 107.9<br>Ag<br>silver<br>47 | 112.4<br>Cd<br>cadmium<br>48 | | | 114.8<br>In<br>indium<br>49 | 118.7<br>Sn<br>tin<br>50 | 121.8<br>Sb<br>antimony<br>51 | 127.6<br>Te<br>tellurium<br>52 | 126.9<br>I<br>iodine<br>53 | 131.3<br>Xe<br>xenon<br>54 |
| 6 | 132.9<br>Cs<br>caesium<br>55 | 137.3<br>Ba<br>barium<br>56 | 138.9<br>La<br>lanthanum<br>57 | 178.5<br>Hf<br>hafnium<br>72 | 180.9<br>Ta<br>tantalum<br>73 | 183.8<br>W<br>tungsten<br>74 | 186.2<br>Re<br>rhenium<br>75 | 190.2<br>Os<br>osmium<br>76 | 192.2<br>Ir<br>iridium<br>77 | 195.1<br>Pt<br>platinum<br>78 | 197.0<br>Au<br>gold<br>79 | 200.6<br>Hg<br>mercury<br>80 | | | 204.4<br>Tl<br>thallium<br>81 | 207.2<br>Pb<br>lead<br>82 | 209.0<br>Bi<br>bismuth<br>83 | [209]<br>Po<br>polonium<br>84 | [210]<br>At<br>astatine<br>85 | [222]<br>Rn<br>radon<br>86 |
| 7 | [223]<br>Fr<br>francium<br>87 | [226]<br>Ra<br>radium<br>88 | [227]<br>Ac<br>actinium<br>89 | [261]<br>Rf<br>rutherfordium<br>104 | [262]<br>Db<br>dubnium<br>105 | [266]<br>Sg<br>seaborgium<br>106 | [264]<br>Bh<br>bohrium<br>107 | [277]<br>Hs<br>hassium<br>108 | [268]<br>Mt<br>meitnerium<br>109 | [271]<br>Ds<br>darmstadtium<br>110 | [272]<br>Rg<br>roentgenium<br>111 | | | | | | | | | |

Elements with atomic numbers 112–116 have been reported but not fully authenticated

| 140.1<br>Ce<br>cerium<br>58 | 140.9<br>Pr<br>praseodymium<br>59 | 144.2<br>Nd<br>neodymium<br>60 | 144.9<br>Pm<br>promethium<br>61 | 150.4<br>Sm<br>samarium<br>62 | 152.0<br>Eu<br>europium<br>63 | 157.2<br>Gd<br>gadolinium<br>64 | 158.9<br>Tb<br>terbium<br>65 | 162.5<br>Dy<br>dysprosium<br>66 | 164.9<br>Ho<br>holmium<br>67 | 167.3<br>Er<br>erbium<br>68 | 168.9<br>Tm<br>thulium<br>69 | 173.0<br>Yb<br>ytterbium<br>70 | 175.0<br>Lu<br>lutetium<br>71 |
|---|---|---|---|---|---|---|---|---|---|---|---|---|---|
| 232<br>Th<br>thorium<br>90 | [231]<br>Pa<br>protactinium<br>91 | 238.1<br>U<br>uranium<br>92 | [237]<br>Np<br>neptunium<br>93 | [242]<br>Pu<br>plutonium<br>94 | [243]<br>Am<br>americium<br>95 | [247]<br>Cm<br>curium<br>96 | [245]<br>Bk<br>berkelium<br>97 | [251]<br>Cf<br>californium<br>98 | [254]<br>Es<br>einsteinium<br>99 | [253]<br>Fm<br>fermium<br>100 | [256]<br>Md<br>mendelevium<br>101 | [254]<br>No<br>nodelium<br>102 | [257]<br>Lr<br>lawrencium<br>103 |